WILD
SPAIN

WILD
SPAIN

The Animals, Plants and Landscapes

TERESA FARINO

Photography by Carlos Sánchez and Teresa Farino

NEW HOLLAND

First published in 2009 by New Holland Publishers (UK) Ltd
London • Cape Town • Sydney • Auckland
www.newhollandpublishers.com

Garfield House, 86–88 Edgware Road, London W2 2EA, UK
80 McKenzie Street, Cape Town 8001, South Africa
Unit 1, 66 Gibbes Street, Chatswood, New South Wales,
Australia 2067
218 Lake Road, Northcote, Auckland, New Zealand

10 9 8 7 6 5 4 3 2 1

ISBN 978 1 84773 126 5

Senior Editor: Krystyna Mayer
Design: Alan Marshall
Cartography: Stephen Dew
Production: Melanie Dowland
Commissioning Editor: Simon Papps
Editorial Direction: Rosemary Wilkinson

COVER AND PRELIMINARY PAGES
Front Cover: Canaries endemic subspecies of Egyptian Vulture
(*Neophron percnopterus majorensis*).
Spine: Iberian Lynx (*Lynx pardinus*).
Back Cover: Brown Bear (*Ursus arctos*).
Page 1: Black Stork (*Ciconia nigra*).
Page 2: Cantabrican Capercaillie (*Tetrao urogallus
cantabricus*), male.
Page 3: Spanish Ibex (*Capra pyrenaica victoriae*), male.
Page 4–5: Cinereous and Griffon Vultures (*Aegypius
monachus* and *Gyps fulvus*) at a carcass.
Page 6, left: Great Bittern (*Botaurus stellaris*); right: Atlantic
Lizard (*Gallotia atlantica*), male.
Page 7, left: the burnet moth *Zygaena contaminei*; right:
Iberian Lynx (*Lynx pardinus*).

Reproduction by Pica Digital (Pte) Ltd, Singapore
Printed and bound in Singapore by Tien Wah Press

CONTENTS

INTRODUCTION

Geographically, Spain can be divided into three distinct units: the mainland, which is part of continental Europe, the Balearic Islands, adrift in the western Mediterranean Sea, and the Canary Islands, a far-flung archipelago in the Atlantic Ocean considerably closer to Africa than to Europe. Spain also possesses several important military outposts in the western Mediterranean, including the Islas Chafarinas and the cities of Ceuta and Melilla on the north Moroccan coast. Spain's north-western shores are exposed to Atlantic weather systems, giving rise to rain-washed, essentially Euro-Siberian habitats, while the bulk of the peninsula and Balearic Islands lie in the Mediterranean climatic domain, with a climax vegetation characterized by dense evergreen forests. The vast upland plateau – the *Meseta* – that occupies the heart of the country is surrounded by important mountain ranges, with the Pyrenees and the Sierra Nevada exceeding 3,000 m. These effectively isolate the *Meseta* from the sea, generating a fundamentally continental climate characterized by long, cold winters and short, sweltering hot summers. Rainfall is scarce here, in extreme cases giving rise to semi-arid enclaves hosting xerophytic vegetation.

LEFT Peña Ubiña, in the San Emiliano Valley, is one of the most westerly outcrops of limestone in the Cordillera Cantábrica.

MAINLAND SPAIN OCCUPIES ABOUT 80 PER CENT of the Iberian Peninsula – a landmass lying at the south-western edge of continental Europe – which it shares with Portugal, Andorra and Gibraltar. It covers around 493,500 sq km, with the Canary Islands adding approximately 7,500 sq km, and the Balearic archipelago a further 5,000 sq km, making Spain the second largest country in Western Europe after France.

The Lie of the Land

Although these days few people would give any credence to the age-old saying that 'Africa begins at the Pyrenees', it is true that this 400-km mountain chain presents a considerable barrier to communications with the rest of Europe, while the southernmost tip of Spain is today separated from Africa by just 15 km of open water, the two landmasses having been linked physically at various times in the past.

More than a fifth of the surface area of mainland Spain and the Balearic archipelago comprises land over 1,000 m in altitude. Three principal mountain chains are positioned around the margins of the peninsula – the Cordillera Cantábrica, the Pyrenees and the Sierras Béticas – with the interior ranges of

the Sistema Central and the Sistema Ibérico completing the picture. The Sierras Béticas continue north-eastwards under the Mediterranean Sea, terminating in the scatter of unsubmerged peaks that today makes up the Balearic archipelago. The Canary Islands, some 1,150 km to the south-west, however, are true oceanic islands – volcanic landmasses that rose from the floor of the Atlantic 20–1.5 million years ago.

While numerous peaks in excess of 3,000 m occur in the Pyrenees and the Sierra Nevada (Sierras Béticas), Spain's highest mountain – El Teide (3,715 m) – is in fact located on the Canary Island of Tenerife. By contrast, only on the coastal plain and in the lower reaches of the Río Guadalquivir can terrain less than 100 m above sea level be found. In terms of mean altitude, Spain is second only to Switzerland among the countries of Western Europe, averaging 650 m above sea level.

The vast bulk of the interior of peninsular Spain comprises two great upland plateaux 600–1,000 m high, separated by the Sistema Central and known collectively as the *Meseta*. The limits of the northern *Meseta* coincide almost exactly with the catchment area of the Río Duero, which does not begin to lose height significantly until it enters Portugal, where it is known as the Douro. The Duero rises in the Picos de Urbión, in the Sistema Ibérico, and flows for some 875 km until it discharges into the Atlantic Ocean at Oporto. The longest river in the Iberian Peninsula is the Tajo (in English, the Tagus and in

BELOW The middle reaches of the mighty Ebro River, near Zaragoza, fringed with gallery forest and backed by an ancient river terrace.

The Topography of Spain

Bay of Biscay

FRANCE

ANDORRA

A Coruña

Oviedo
Torre Cerredo
(2,648 m)
Picos de Europa
Cordillera Cantábrica

Bilbao

Pamplona

Pyrenees

Aneto
(3,404 m)

Andorra la Vella

Golfo de
Roses

Río Miño
Río Sil
Montes de León
León

Vitoria
Sierra de
La Demanda

Río Arga
Río Ebro
Río Gállego
Río Cinca
Río Llobregat

Cordilleras Costero-Catalanas

Barcelona

Río Esla
Burgos
Sierra del
Moncayo

Sistema Ibérica

Río Pisuerga
Valladolid
Río Duero

Moncayo
(2,313 m)
Zaragoza

Río Ebro

Key
▲ Peaks

Río Tormes
P 149
Salamanca

Sierra de
Somosierra

Elevation
Over 1,000 m
600–1,000 m
100–600 m
0–100 m

Sierra de
Guadarrama
Río Tajuña

Madrid

Sierra de Gredos
Almanzor
(2,591 m)

Sierra de Gata

Río Tajo
Serranía
de Cuenca

Sierra de
Albarracín

Río Turia
Río Mijares

Sierra de
Javalambre

Islas Baleares

Menorca

Puig Major
(1,445 m)

Palma

Mallorca

PORTUGAL

Sierra de
San Pedro
Sierra de
Guadalupe
Montes de Toledo

Río Tajo

Río Júcar

València
Golfo de
València

Ibiza/Eivissa

Formentera

Lisboa

Río Guadiana
Sierra de Almadén

Albacete

Río Ardila
Sierra de Aracena
Sierra Morena
Sierra Madrona

Cordillera Subbética
Sierra de Segura
Río Segura

Murcia

Mediterranean
Sea

Río Guadalquivir
Córdoba

Sistemas Béticos
Río Guadalentín

N

Sevilla

Granada
Mulhacén (3,479 m)
Sierra Nevada

Golfo de Cádiz
Serranía
de Ronda
Málaga
P 45
Cádiz

Strait of Gibraltar
Ceuta

Melilla

ATLANTIC
OCEAN

MOROCCO

0   50   100   150   200 km

Islas Canarias

ATLANTIC

OCEAN

Lanzarote

La Palma
Roque de los
Muchachos
(2,426 m)

Tenerife
Santa Cruz

Fuerteventura

La Gomera
Teide
(3,715 m)

Garajonay
(1,487 m)

Las Palmas

Pico de las Nieves
(1,949 m)

El Hierro

Gran Canaria

0   50   100 km

Portuguese, the Tejo), which again flows westwards, entering the Atlantic at Lisboa, so that its 1,007 km are shared between Spain and Portugal. Other major rivers heading towards the Atlantic include the exclusively Spanish Guadiana (818 km), which rises in the Lagunas de Ruidera (Castilla–La Mancha) then follows the Spanish–Portuguese border southwards until it hits the south-western Iberian coast; and the Guadalquivir (657 km), whose source lies in the Sierra de Cazorla and exit point on the eastern margin of the Doñana National Park.

By contrast, only 30 per cent of Spain's catchment areas collect waters that ultimately discharge into the Mediterranean, with that of the Ebro – at 910 km, the longest river entirely in Spanish territory – making up the lion's share, followed by the Júcar (498 km) and Segura (325 km).

Peninsular Spain's rather convoluted coastline is almost 5,000 km long, of which the Cantabrican shore, between France and Spain's northernmost point at Estaca de Bares (A Coruña), measures 1,086 km, the Atlantic shores of Galicia and Andalucía making up 1,728 km and the Mediterranean coast 2,058 km. The Balearic Islands add a further 1,429 km of coastline to this total, more than 40 per cent of which belongs to Mallorca, with the Canary archipelago shores measuring 1,583 km, over half of which pertains to Fuerteventura, Gran Canaria and Tenerife.

The Autonomous Communities and Provinces of Spain

FRANCE

Bizkaia Gipuzkoa

ANDORRA
■ Andorra la Vella

N

A Coruña

A Coruña
Lugo

1

Pontevedra

Ourense

Asturias
2 •Oviedo

Cantabria
3

Bilbao•
4
Araba

Pamplona•
Navarra

6

Huesca

Lleida

Girona
8
•Girona

Barcelona
•Barcelona

León
León•

Palencia

Burgos
Burgos

5
La Rioja

Zaragoza•
7
Zaragoza

Tarragona

Zamora

Valladolid
10
•Valladolid

Soria

Teruel

Castelló

Islas Baleares

ATLANTIC OCEAN

Salamanca
Salamanca

Segovia

Ávila

11
Madrid
■Madrid

Guadalajara
•Guadalajara

Menorca

Palma•

Mallorca

Cuenca
•Cuenca

9

PORTUGAL

Cáceres
Cáceres•

Toledo
Toledo•

Ibiza/Eivissa

Arxipèlag de Cabrera

Lisboa
■

Badajoz•
12
•Mérida
Badajoz

Ciudad Real
•Ciudad Real

Albacete
•Albacete

13

València
•València

14

Formentera

Alacant
•Alacant

Córdoba
•Córdoba

Jaén
•Jaén

Murcia
•Murcia
15

Mediterranean Sea

Huelva

Sevilla
Sevilla•

16

Granada
•Granada

Almería
•Almería

Cádiz
Cádiz•

Málaga
•Málaga

•Ceuta

Melilla•

MOROCCO

Autonomous Communities

1	Galicia
2	Asturias
3	Cantabria
4	País Vasco (Euskadi)
5	La Rioja
6	Navarra
7	Aragón
8	Catalunya
9	Islas Baleares
10	Castilla y León
11	Madrid
12	Extremadura
13	Castilla-La Mancha
14	País Valencià
15	Murcia
16	Andalucía
17	Canarias

0   50   100   150   200 km

Islas Canarias

La Palma

Lanzarote

17
Tenerife

Santa Cruz•

Tenerife

Las Palmas•

Fuerteventura

La Gomera

Gran Canaria

El Hierro

0   50   100 km

Climate

Located between the Atlantic Ocean and the Mediterranean Sea, the Iberian Peninsula's climatic conditions are associated with both, although the interior reaches are characterized by a more continental regime. The distant Canary Islands, on the other hand, are subject to a warmer, subtropical climate, with distinctive vegetation and animal life.

The Atlantic Regime

Influenced by rain-laden depressions sweeping in from the Atlantic all year round, north-western Spain is said to be one of the cloudiest regions on Earth. Strong westerly winds carry damp, cloudy air inland, giving rise to frequent mists and an annual precipitation of about 1,600 mm, although this decreases somewhat heading east towards the French border. The abundant rains are distributed throughout the year, with slight maxima in spring and autumn.

To a considerable extent, the air temperature is dependent upon the temperature of the adjacent ocean – which is relatively warm in winter and cool in summer – so the annual fluctuation between seasons can be as little as 10ºC. Although the winters are cold, with average temperatures generally reaching less than 10ºC, frosts are almost unknown in the coastal rea-

ches, while summers are mild, with a mean approaching 20°C. Due to the almost constant cloud cover, insolation and evaporation levels are low, and as a result sufficient soil water is available for plant growth to continue right through the summer. Not surprisingly, the northern territories of Galicia, Asturias, Cantabria and the País Vasco are frequently referred to as 'Green Spain'.

The Cordillera Cantábrica – running almost parallel to the northern Spanish coast for much of its length – presents a major barrier to these Atlantic depressions, so rainfall and air humidity decrease dramatically to the south. In essence, this mountain chain forms the boundary between the Atlantic and Mediterranean climatic zones in Spain, although a transitional sub-Mediterranean belt traverses the country just to the south, extending from the north-eastern corner of Portugal to the Catalan Pyrenees.

Mediterranean Climate

Across much of the eastern and southern reaches of the Iberian Peninsula, as well as in the Balearic archipelago, mild, moist winters are the norm, with average temperatures of around 10°C. At the end of September, Atlantic depressions start to penetrate deep into the Mediterranean region, bringing cooler

ABOVE The spectacularly tilted limestone strata of the Ordesa National Park, in the Aragonese Pyrenees.

weather, clouds and rain. This precipitation falls throughout the autumn, winter and spring, varying annually between 400 and 800 mm, and is usually highest in the country's western reaches. Even so, rainfall is irregular – on average, there are only 100 rainy days in Mediterranean Spain each year – and typified by short, heavy storms followed by long periods of clear weather.

By contrast, between the end of May and mid-September, Mediterranean summers are cloudless, sunny and hot, and characterized by a pronounced period of drought. Average summer temperatures typically exceed 20°C, often approaching 30°C in the southernmost reaches of Spain, where about 2,500 hours of sunshine are recorded each year. It stands to reason, therefore, that the main periods of plant growth coincide with the spring and autumn, with many of the herbaceous species dying back in summer.

Semi-arid Regions

Located within Mediterranean Spain are regions where the climate is even hotter and drier than is typical of the Mediterranean. In Almería and Murcia, for example, in the extreme south-east, average precipitation is rarely more than 250 mm per year, while maximum summer temperatures can reach almost 50°C. Due to the 3,000-plus hours of sunshine per year and the periodic hot, dry *sirocco* winds that sweep up from North Africa, evaporation levels are extremely high, so that the amount of water remaining in the soil is minimal and semi-desert conditions prevail.

The central heartland of Spain, far from the ameliorating effects of either the Atlantic or the Mediterranean, experiences an essentially continental climate. Rainfall is scarce and long, bitter winters alternate with short, hot summers: a state of affairs described as 'nine months of winter and three of hell' by its inhabitants. Temperatures may range from minus 20°C to more than 45°C over the course of the year, and even on a daily basis fluctuations can be extreme. Furthermore, in parts of the Ebro Depression, annual precipitation rarely exceeds 300 mm, creating arid habitats similar to those of south-eastern Spain.

Mountain Weather

This very general picture is complicated by the fact that Spain is riddled with mountain ranges. As a rule of thumb, precipitation is higher on mountain slopes oriented towards the prevailing winds, while the lee slopes lie in the so-called 'rain shadow'. Because air temperature decreases with altitude – by around 0.6°C per 100 m – the high mountains of both Atlantic and Mediterranean Spain experience a considerably colder climate than the surrounding areas, and much of the winter precipitation falls as snow. As an example, in the Sierra Nevada in mid-summer, the air temperature at the top of Mulhacén (3,479 m) can be as little as 15°C, while temperatures in the 40s scorch the adjacent semi-desert regions of Almería.

The Canary Islands

Located about 100 km off the west coast of Africa and some 1,100 km to the south of the Iberian Peninsula, the Canary Islands are subject to an oceanic, subtropical climate, moderated in summer by the effects of the cool, south-flowing Canary Current. Throughout the archipelago, the climate is mild and frost-free at lower levels, with average air temperatures over the course of the year ranging from 18 to 26°C. As always, however, temperatures decrease with altitude, so that Tenerife's El Teide (3,715 m) is snow-clad for several months of the year, frequently experiencing a diurnal temperature range of around 25°C.

The more westerly reaches of the Canary Islands are exposed to the passage of Atlantic depressions, particularly in winter, giving an average rainfall of up to 800 mm annually, most of which falls between November and March. These relatively mountainous western isles also catch the full force of the North East Trade Winds, here called *alisios*, for much of the year. As a result, their northern slopes are wreathed more or less permanently in damp cloud at 500–1,200 m, permitting the continued existence of the semi-tropical laurel forests that

covered much of Spain during the Tertiary period. By contrast, the low-lying eastern isles of Fuerteventura and Lanzarote intercept the *alisios* only at their highest peaks – Pico de la Zarza on Fuerteventura (807 m) and the Peñas del Chache on Lanzarote (671 m) – so elsewhere on the islands the annual precipitation rarely exceeds 100 mm and drought-tolerant vegetation is the norm. In addition, these eastern islands are frequently exposed to a hot, dusty wind, the *calima*, which originates in the Sahara. This considerably boosts air temperatures and produces summer mean temperatures of up to 35°C.

Historical Context

Recent archaeological discoveries in the Sierra de Atapuerca, a small, rather unprepossessing limestone hill about 15 km east of Burgos, suggest that its labyrinth of underground caverns has provided shelter for various species of hominid for something in the region of a million years. Fragments of bone from at least six individuals, thought to be around 800,000 years old and quite unlike any other human remains, have been described as *Homo antecessor*, from the Latin for 'explorer'. Other remains at Atapuerca date from 350,000–500,000 years ago, pertaining to hominids of a robust stature, with the average male around 1.68 m tall. These are of a different lineage from that of *H. antecessor* and have been classified tentatively as *H. heidelbergensis*, although they also bear a resemblance to Neanderthal Man (*H. neanderthalensis*) and may even be his direct ancestor.

Neanderthal Man proper is thought to have lived 120,000–30,000 years ago, when he was replaced throughout Europe by our direct ancestor, Cro-Magnon Man (*H. sapiens*). These early hunter–gatherers had little impact on the vast forests that dominated the Spanish landscape at the time, so that evidence of their occupation is negligible, although the cave system of Altamira in Cantabria contains paintings of such splendour that their authenticity was doubted for several decades. Thought to be almost 15,000 years old, these paintings employ red, yellow and brown ochres accentuated with black manganese earth and charcoal, and depict the animals with which these primitive peoples shared their world, predominantly bison, but also horses, deer and boar.

During Neolithic times – in Europe, 4000–2400 BC – our ancestors became more sedentary creatures, developing the skills necessary to grow crops and domesticate wild animals. Their activities heralded the start of the widespread deforestation that has left Spain with less than 10 per cent of its original woodland cover today.

Nowadays it is widely speculated that the Basques are the direct descendents of these early peoples, but for the most part present-day Spaniards hail from a diverse range of external cul-

OPPOSITE The precipitous Riscos de Famara, in northern Lanzarote, with La Graciosa and other islets of the Archipiélago Chinojo beyond.

TOP The arid plains around the Laguna de Gallocanta play host to enormous flocks of merino sheep in the winter.

BOTTOM Since the Middle Ages, olive groves have replaced much of the primeval Mediterranean forest on lime-rich soils in hilly terrain.

tures. During historic times, Spain has been invaded by Iberos from North Africa, Phoenicians from the eastern Mediterranean (12th century BC), Celts from central Europe (800–600 BC), Greeks (7th century BC) and Romans (2nd century BC). Roman hegemony in the Iberian Peninsula lasted until AD 409, at which point it was shattered by a new wave of invasions from central Europe, spearheaded by the Vandals, Swabians and Alans.

The most significant incursion, however, was undoubtedly that of the Moors in 711. In just five years, these North African Muslims took control of virtually the entire Iberian Peninsula, with the exception of a few remote mountain enclaves in Asturias and Cantabria. The Christian struggle to reconquer Spain, by contrast, lasted almost eight centuries, concluding with the fall of Granada in 1492. In fact, much of the culture

that is nowadays considered to be quintessentially Spanish has its origins in this long period of Moorish occupation.

With each successive invasion, the Spanish forests were eroded by the need for timber, firewood and the clearance of land to cultivate crops to feed the burgeoning population. In addition, the introduction of the merino sheep by the Moors led to the creation of extensive rangelands, including the wood–pasture known as *dehesa* (see page 42).

Spain's more recent history is punctuated by a number of equally barbarous wars, culminating in the Spanish Civil War of 1936–9, the upshot of which was a fascist dictatorship that lasted for almost 40 years and ended only with the death of Francisco Franco in 1975. During this time, Spain was very much isolated from the outside world. As a result, the technological advances in agriculture that ravaged the natural habitats and wildlife of other parts of Europe barely touched the Spanish countryside.

Following the restoration of the monarchy, much of the responsibility for government has devolved to the regions, with the new Constitution in 1978 defining no less than 17

autonomous communities. Access to the European Economic Community in 1986 unfortunately gave Spain access to external funding for some of the most environmentally damaging large-scale infrastructure projects ever to have taken place. Meanwhile widespread agricultural intensification led to the indiscriminate use of pesticides and artificial fertilizers, extensive wetland drainage and the replacement of millions of hectares of ancient olive groves and *dehesas* with cereal monocultures, all in the name of 'progress'.

Present-day Demography

By 2007, the population of Spain was in the region of 45 million people, a considerable increase from the 1975 figure of 35 million. During the 21st century alone, Spain's population has increased by some 5 million people, for the most part due to immigration from other European countries and Spanish-speaking parts of South and Central America; around 10 per cent of Spain's inhabitants are of foreign nationality. These days, the vast majority of the population is concentrated either

ABOVE 'Sundial-like' Western Holm Oaks are the predominant trees in the *dehesas* of the Monfragüe National Park.

OVERLEAF Almería is perhaps the hottest, driest region of Spain, with semi-desert habitats prevailing away from the coast.

in the principal cities of the coastal regions, particularly in Andalucía and Catalunya, or in and around Madrid, the capital city whose metropolitan area is home to more than 3 million people.

Overall population density lies at around 90 inhabitants per square kilometre. However, because more than 10,000 people are crammed into each square kilometre of some Spanish cities, large tracts of remote mountain terrain and arid lands of the interior are virtually uninhabited.

As an example, the autonomous communities of Castilla–La Mancha, Aragón and Extremadura all possess average population densities of approximately 25 inhabitants per square kilometre. Not surprisingly, it is these least populated regions that are home to Spain's best-preserved habitats and finest assemblages of wildlife.

Chapter I

HABITATS AND VEGETATION

Mainland Spain occupies the lion's share of the roughly square Iberian Peninsula, located at the extreme south-western edge of Europe just a stone's throw from Africa. The formidable mountain ranges of the Pyrenees, Cordillera Cantábrica and Sierras Béticas almost completely surround a high upland plateau known as the *Meseta*, which is itself split in two by the east–west oriented Sistema Central. Several major rivers traverse the *Meseta*, the Ebro flowing east into the Mediterranean and the Duero, Tajo, Guadiana and Guadalquivir running westwards towards the Atlantic, while continental still waters range from glacial lakes to shallow endorheic lagoons. Spain's convoluted coastline is more than 8,000 km long, and comprises rocky shores backed by precipitous cliffs, sweeping expanses of sandy beach and dune systems, and more scattered enclaves of salt marsh and mudflats at the mouths of rivers. More than 1,000 km to the south, the unique habitats of the volcanic Canary archipelago have more in common with Africa than Spain, ranging from arid badlands at sea level through extensive conifer and laurel forests to high-altitude vegetation at more than 3,000 m.

LEFT Red Deer (*Cervus elaphus*) in the savannah-like grasslands of the Cabañeros National Park.

MOUNTAINS

Because of their steep slopes and relative inaccessibility, the world's high mountains harbour some of the best-preserved natural ecosystems on the planet, rich in plant and animal life. As might be expected, many of Spain's most diverse protected areas are located in mountainous regions.

Climbing a Spanish mountain can be compared to undertaking a journey from Europe's most southerly latitudes to the Arctic Circle. For every 150 m ascended, the temperature drops by approximately 1°C, until there comes a point at which winter precipitation falls as snow rather than rain. Levels of insolation and ultraviolet radiation tend to increase with altitude, as do wind strength and speed, while the amount of oxygen in the air diminishes. Generally speaking, with increasing altitude the summers become cooler and the winters longer and colder, so that the period during which plants are able to grow, reproduce and store sufficient energy to survive the next winter gets progressively shorter.

OPPOSITE The enigmatic volcanic outcrops known as the Roques de García, in the Cañadas del Teide National Park.
BELOW Carpets of Alpenrose can be found on siliceous bedrock in the subalpine zone of the Pyrenees.

Vegetation Zonation

In response to these changing environmental conditions, distinct belts of vegetation occur at different altitudes, each dominated by a suite of plants supremely adapted to cope with the prevailing climatic milieu. As a rule of thumb, the lower slopes are clothed with broadleaved deciduous trees that require a physiological growth period of at least four months with temperatures above 10°C. Any less, and they are replaced by more hardy evergreen coniferous trees – pines (*Pinus* spp.) and firs (*Abies* spp.) – but even so, when the physiological growth period drops below three months, the season's new needles do not have time to mature enough to survive the rigours of winter.

Thus, one of the most significant changes in montane vegetation occurs where the climate becomes so harsh that tree growth becomes untenable. This level is commonly referred to as the tree-line, above which only low shrubs and herbaceous perennials can survive. Because temperatures increase with proximity to the equator, the tree-line generally lies at higher altitudes in southern Spain than in the north, but in many areas has been artificially lowered by felling, grazing and fire.

The vegetation zone just above the tree-line is generally called the subalpine zone, the natural climax community of which typically comprises a diverse assemblage of shrubs. On siliceous soils in the valley of Benasque, in the Aragonese Pyrenees, for example, clumps of the Alpenrose (*Rhododendron ferrugineum*) are interspersed with the Dwarf Juniper (*Juniperus communis* ssp. *alpina*) and Bilberry (*Vaccinium myrtillus*). By contrast, in the drier, lime-rich mountains of southern and eastern Spain, the subalpine zone is populated by so-called 'hedgehog heaths': assemblages of cushion-shaped, spiny shrubs such as *Hormathophylla spinosa* and *Vella spinosa* (Cruciferae), Hedgehog Broom (*Erinacea anthyllis*) and Spiny Hare's-ear (*Bupleurum frutescens* ssp. *spinosum*).

The true alpine zone in Spain starts at about 2,300 m, and is best represented in the Sierra Nevada, the Pyrenees and on El Teide, on the Canary island of Tenerife, all of which exceed this height by a thousand metres or more. The Sierra Nevada covers some 2,000 sq km and is the most significant mountain range in south-west Europe, incorporating not only the highest peak in mainland Spain, Mulhacén, at 3,479 m, but also a further dozen or so summits in excess of 3,000 m. Even though the last permanent glaciers here succumbed to increasing global temperatures at the end of the 20th century, this ice-sculpted landscape is still riddled with moraines, cirques and

ABOVE *Globularia repens* is a prostrate species of limestone outcrops in the mountains of northern Spain.

glacial lakes. Today the only Spanish glaciers are found in the high Pyrenees – just 3.5 sq km of permanent ice distributed across 15 nuclei – the most extensive of which is located on the northern flanks of Aneto, the highest mountain of the range, at 3,404 m.

Hotspots of Biodiversity

During the Pleistocene ice ages, the cryophilic flora and fauna of the world's boreal and Arctic regions ventured as far south as the Mediterranean. When the last ice sheets retreated around 10,000 years ago, these northern species found themselves unsuited to the increasingly warm climate of the lowlands and were forced to retreat into the highest mountains, where they were effectively cut off from neighbouring populations. Not surprisingly, ten millennia of evolution in isolation have given rise to a high degree of endemism among the flora and fauna of Spain's highest mountains.

The Sierra Nevada is a superb illustration of this, harbouring more than 80 unique invertebrate taxa and about 70 species of vascular plant that occur nowhere else in the world. Many of the Sierra Nevada's endemic plants are high-altitude species that are becoming increasingly rare as temperatures rise: the sandwort *Arenaria nevadensis*, the stork's-bill *Erodium rupicola*, the butterwort *Pinguicula nevadensis* and the composites *Leontodon microcephalus*, *Senecio elodes*, *S. nevadensis* and *Artemisia granatensis*, the latter only found above 3,000 m. The 400 km-long Pyrenean chain that separates France from Spain is yet another notable botanical hotspot, with some 3,500 species of vascular plant, around 180 of which are unique to the range.

Plant Adaptations

Above the tree-line, most plants grow close to the ground so as to avoid the worst of the wind and to receive some protection from severe frosts by sheltering beneath the insulating layer of snow during the winter months, since beneath a half metre-thick layer of snow the temperature rarely falls below -1°C at ground level, even if the air temperature is 30°C below zero.

Some evergreen shrubs – like the Alpenrose, for example – adopt a cushion-like habit, in the heart of which the temperature may be as much as 10°C higher than externally. Other evergreen shrubs – like *Globularia repens* and the Crowberry (*Empetrum nigrum*) – are prostrate, mat-forming species. In the Spanish Pyrenees, the highest altitude at which shrubs can grow is around 3,100 m. Here they are represented by Dwarf and Net-leaved Willows (*Salix herbacea* and *S. reticulata*), Mountain Avens (*Dryas octopetala*) and Trailing Azalea (*Loiseleuria procumbens*), all of which are low, creeping species equally at home to the north of the Arctic Circle.

Herbaceous perennials, by contrast, tend to die back at the end of summer, either storing energy reserves for the following season in underground organs, or producing low-level over-wintering buds at the end of the summer, which again are protected by the insulating blanket of snow. Some of the earliest species to bloom are bulbs, which appear as soon as the snow melts – for example the daffodils *Narcissus nevadensis* in the Sierra Nevada and *N. asturiensis* in the Cordillera Cantábrica, and crocuses such as *Crocus nevadensis* in the mountains of eastern and southern Spain, *C. carpetanus* in northern and central Spain, and the White Crocus (*C. vernus* ssp. *albiflorus*) in the Pyrenees.

Because the brief growing season generally does not allow them time to complete their life cycles from seed, annual plants make up less than 4 per cent of the Spanish alpine flora. The annual species found at the greatest altitude in Spain is the stonecrop *Sedum candollei*, which sometimes reaches heights of 3,000 m. Studies have shown that the period between the first bud appearing and the maturation of the seeds can be as little as 22 days.

Because of the relative paucity of insects in the alpine zone, many flowers of plants growing here are disproportionately large and brightly coloured, so as to give them the best possible chance of attracting a pollinator. Some outstanding examples of this type of 'giantism' are the Alpine Avens (*Geum montanum*), Trumpet Gentian (*Gentiana acaulis*) and Pyrenean Pheasant's-eye (*Adonis pyrenaica*).

In other cases, dozens of smaller flowers are packed tightly together to give the overall impression of a much larger bloom, as can be seen in cushion-forming species such as the Moss Campion (*Silene acaulis*), Pyrenean Whitlow-grass (*Petrocallis pyrenaica*) and vividly pink-flowered rock-jasmine *Androsace ciliata*, the latter possibly the species to reach the highest altitude in mainland Spain, growing just below the summit of

GENTIANS

Perhaps the best-known of all mountain plants are gentians (genus *Gentiana*), around 300 species of which are distributed across the polar and temperate regions of both hemispheres. All the European gentians – about 30 species – have blue, purple or yellow flowers, usually pollinated by bees and butterflies. Sixteen species of *Gentiana* are known from Spain, plus four very similar *Gentianella* species.

Among the most striking species in this group are the trumpet gentians, which have fabulous deep-blue flowers that are each as much as 7 cm long and emerge from a tiny basal rosette. The alpine pastures and rock gardens of the Pyrenees and Cordillera Cantábrica host the Trumpet Gentian, Pyrenean Trumpet Gentian (*G. angustifolia*), *G. occidentalis*, Clusius's Gentian (*G. clusii*) and Southern Gentian (*G. alpina*). In a classic case of disjunct distribution, Southern Gentians are also found more than 600 km away in the Sierra Nevada.

Great Yellow Gentians (*G. lutea*), and the Pyrenean endemics *G. montserratii* and *G. burseri*, have clusters of yellow flowers arranged in whorls around stems up to a metre tall. Great Yellow Gentians are found in all the central and southern European mountains, with a Spanish distribution that takes in the mountains of the north, the Sistema Central and the Sierra Nevada. The roots have long been collected for their tonic properties and were formerly used to flavour liqueurs, although this practice is now prohibited by European law in order to protect wild populations. The Cross Gentian (*G. cruciata*), which occurs in the Pyrenees and Sistema Ibérico in Spain, is another robust species, this time with four-lobed, rather dull slate-blue flowers; it is the larval food plant of the Spanish populations of the Mountain Alcon Blue butterfly (*Maculinea rebeli*).

Gentians typical of rather wetter habitats include the widespread Marsh Gentian (*G. pneumonanthe*), the Spanish endemic *G. boryi*, with pale blue flowers and a patchy distribution that takes in the Cordillera Cantábrica, the Sierra de Gredos and the Sierra Nevada, and the Pyrenean Gentian (*G. pyrenaica*), whose clumps of ten-lobed, deep-purple flowers grace acid, boggy habitats in the eastern Pyrenees.

BELOW Trumpet Gentians have relatively huge flowers to attract pollinating insects, which are scarce in the high mountains.

BELOW Pyrenean Gentians are the only purple-flowered members of the genus *Gentiana* in Spain.

Aneto, at the veritable apex of the Pyrenees. Many of the high-altitude perennials do not rely solely on this rather hit-and-miss method of seed production to ensure their survival, however, but also reproduce by vegetative means, sending out runners or rhizomes to generate new plants, while in the Alpine Bistort (*Polygonum viviparum*) some flowers have been replaced by bulbils that simply drop off and grow into independent plants. Other so-called apomictic species, such as some of the lady's-mantles (*Alchemilla* spp.), have also dispensed with the need for pollinators and are able to produce viable seed without their flowers being fertilized.

Many mountain plants possess exceedingly hairy leaves. The hairs trap a layer of air around the leaf, providing insulation in winter and reducing air movement – and so lessening water loss by transpiration – in summer. They also reflect the sun's rays and thus afford protection against excessive ultra-violet radiation. Perhaps the best-known European mountain plant exhibiting this feature is the Edelweiss (*Leontopodium alpinum*), confined to the Pyrenees in Spain, with other Spanish examples including the cinquefoil *Potentilla nivalis*, Yellow Genipi (*Artemisia umbelliformis*) and Sierra Nevada endemic Snow Plantain (*Plantago nivalis*).

Alpine Rock Gardens

At a casual glance, much of the terrain in the alpine zone appears to be simply bare rock. Only where soil accumulates in crevices are plants able to take root, but even here nutrient levels are low and available water is strictly limited.

Throughout the Spanish mountains, the diversity of these chasmophyte communities is very high and they are riddled with rare and endemic species. Typical plants of limestone rock gardens in the Pyrenees are the Green Spleenwort

(*Asplenium viride*), Swiss Rock-jasmine (*Androsace helvetica*), Common Houseleek (*Sempervivum tectorum*), a whole host of saxifrages (see page 92), the Pyrenean Bellflower (*Campanula speciosa*) and the delightful Ramonda (*Ramonda myconi*). With their densely hairy, heart-shaped leaves and yellow-eyed, purple flowers, Ramondas are among the most emblematic of all the flowers growing in the Pyrenees, particularly favouring shady limestone cliffs.

Plants that are more characteristic of siliceous rocks in the Pyrenees are the Rock Campion (*Silene rupestris*), Mountain Houseleek (*Sempervivum montanum*), *Androsace vandellii* and a different suite of saxifrages, namely French, Scented-leaved and Yellow Mountain Saxifrages (*Saxifraga clusii, S. intricata* and *S. aizoides*).

Meanwhile the rock gardens of the Sierra de Gredos are studded with clumps of Rock Lady's-mantle (*Alchemilla saxatilis*), the thrift *America bigerrensis* and the snapdragon *Antirrhinum grosii*.

Screes

Screes – sloping accumulations of rock debris at the foot of cliffs – are even less hospitable environments for plant growth, yet some species are supremely adapted to these unstable habitats. Typical scree plants possess flexible stems and immensely powerful root systems, as well as the facility to produce new plants from fragments that get broken off when the screes shift. The diminutive Alpine Milk-vetch (*Astragalus alpinus*), for example, may have roots up to 1.5 m long.

Emblematic limestone scree plants in northern Spain are the Pyrenean Columbine (*Aquilegia pyrenaica*), Parnassus-leaved Buttercup (*Ranunculus parnassiifolius*), Spoon-leaved

Candytuft (*Iberis spathulata*), Pyrenean Vetch (*Vicia pyrenaica*), Xatardia (*Xatardia scabra*), Alpine Skullcap (*Scutellaria alpina*), Alpine Toadflax (*Linaria alpina*), Pyrenean Speedwell (*Veronica nummularia*), Pygmy Hawk's-beard (*Crepis pygmaea*), Large-flowered Leopard's-bane (*Doronicum grandiflorum*) and Pyrenean Yam (*Borderea pyrenaica*).

In the Sierra Nevada, acid screes at the highest altitudes are colonized by the endemic pinkish-flowered, cushion-forming violet *Viola crassiuscula*, *Chaenorhinum glareosum* and Glacier Toadflax (*Linaria glacialis*), while the Arctic–Alpine Pyrenean Poppy (*Papaver lapeyrousianum*) occurs both here and in the Pyrenees, but nowhere in between. Among the pinnacles of the Sierra de Gredos (the highest peak is Almanzor, at 2,591 m), granite screes harbour a unique assemblage of central Iberian endemics, including the mignonette *Reseda gredensis*, the figwort *Scophularia reuteri* and the lavender cotton *Santolina oblongifolia*.

Animal Adaptations

Many high-altitude invertebrates, amphibians and reptiles possess extremely high levels of pigmentation in the cuticle or skin, often appearing almost black. Such colouration is thought to serve two purposes: firstly, to absorb heat, enabling creatures that are unable to control their body temperature internally to remain active in cold habitats, and secondly to provide protection from high levels of ultraviolet radiation. As an example, the essentially montane butterflies of the genus *Erebia*, which is represented by 19 species in Spain, possess deep-brown upper wings.

In order to retain as much heat as possible in winter, small mammals of mountain environments have small ears, short limbs and a body shape tending to the spherical. The Snow Vole (*Chionomys nivalis*) and Alpine Marmot (*Marmota marmota*) provide classic examples of this configuration. Alpine Marmots are among the few Spanish mammals that truly hibernate to avoid the worst of the winter weather. While snow lies thick on the ground, they huddle in small groups in underground burrows, entering a lethargic state in which their body temperature drops by around 5°C, their basic bodily functions being provided for by reserves of subcutaneous fat that were accumulated during the summer months. By contrast, Snow Voles and other small mammals of the Spanish mountains, such as the Common Shrew (*Sorex araneus*), remain active throughout the winter, foraging for shoots and leaves under the protective carpet of snow.

In winter, when the high pastures are covered in thick snow, large herbivores such as the Southern Chamois

LEFT, ABOVE The Spanish population of the Rock Ptarmigan numbers just a few hundred pairs, confined to the alpine zone of the Pyrenees.
LEFT, BELOW Alpine Marmots live in family groups consisting of the adult pair and their offspring of the past two or three seasons.

(*Rupicapra pyrenaica*) and Spanish Ibex (*Capra pyrenaica*) must migrate to lower levels in search of food. The same can be said of that archetypal high-altitude bird the Wallcreeper (*Tichodroma muralis*), which in winter descends from the peaks to dwell among crags and gorges in the lowlands. Similarly, Yellow- and Red-billed Choughs (*Pyrrhocorax graculus* and *P. pyrrhocorax*) often feed in middle-altitude meadows and pastures in winter, forming large mixed flocks. Curiously, the predominantly seed-eating Snow Finch (*Montifringilla nivalis*) of the Pyrenees and Cordillera Cantábrica tends to remain in the high mountains all year round, despite the apparent lack of available food.

Southern Chamois and Spanish Ibex moult in the autumn, exchanging their fine summer coats for a thick, shaggy pelt that is ideal for coping with cold, damp winter conditions. More impressive, however, is the way in which some mountain creatures change the colour of their fur or feathers in winter, the better to blend in with their surroundings. Stoats (*Mustela*

ABOVE Male Spanish Ibex possess fabulous lyre-shaped horns that reach a length of 70–90 cm by the age of 12–15 years.

erminea), for example, become pure white Ermines in winter, the camouflage so provided enabling them to ambush their quarry more effectively. Similarly, the Rock Ptarmigan (*Lagopus mutus*) acquires a glossy white plumage in late autumn, which permits it to blend in with the winter snows and therefore avoid predators.

For a small creature, wings can be a distinct disadvantage where strong winds are an everyday occurrence, so it is not surprising that many high-mountain insects have given up on flight as a bad job. This means that such creatures must be much more sedentary, and are thus very vulnerable to changes in habitat. Among the rarest endemic invertebrates of the Sierra Nevada are the flightless bush-cricket *Baetica ustulata*, confined to just a handful of 10 x 10 km squares, and the related *Ephippigerida paulinoi*, which is scarcely more widespread.

ABOVE The Apollo is one of Spain's largest butterflies, with a wingspan of up to 85 mm.

Mountain Butterflies

What *is* surprising is that so many butterflies inhabit alpine habitats across Spain, when one would think that these fragile insects would find it hard to cope with the rigours of the high mountain environment. The truth of the matter is that, like mountain plants, most species survive the winter as eggs or very small caterpillars, protected under the insulating carpet of

BELOW On the wing from late June to August, Mountain Clouded Yellows favour pastures and rock gardens above 1,700 m.

snow, the adult insects emerging only when climatic conditions are at their optimum in high summer. Spain's mountain ranges literally teem with butterflies that do not occur in lowland habitats, with one of the most characteristic species being the fabulous saucer-sized Apollo (*Parnassius apollo*), whose caterpillars feed principally on stonecrops (*Sedum* spp.). Each of the principal Spanish massifs harbours one or more unique subspecies.

Perhaps the greatest diversity of Spanish high-altitude butterflies is found in the Pyrenees, where the Apollo is typically accompanied by the Clouded Apollo (*Parnassius mnemosyne*), Alpine Grizzled Skipper (*Pyrgus andromedae*), Mountain Clouded Yellow (*Colias phicomone*), Mountain Dappled White (*Euchloe simplonia*), Peak White (*Pontia callidice*), Mountain Alcon Blue, Gavarnie Blue (*Agriades pyrenaicus*), Glandon Blue (*A. glandon*), Eros Blue (*Polyommatus eros*), Mountain Fritillary (*Boloria napaea*) and Shepherd's Fritillary (*B. pales pyrenemiscens*). The Pyrenees are additionally home to an entire host of ringlets belonging to the genus *Erebia*, including Mountain, Silky, Dewy and Lefèbvre's Ringlets (*E. epiphron, E. gorge, E. pandrose* and *E. lefebvrei*), as well as a number of species restricted to the French and Spanish flanks of the mountain chain: Gavarnie, False Dewy and Pyrenees Brassy Ringlets (*E. gorgone, E. sthennyo* and *E. rondoui*).

Above 2,500 m in the Sierra Nevada, butterflies that accompany the Apollo (here the subspecies *Parnassius apollo nevadensis*) include species unique to the range such as Zullich's Blue (*Agriades zullichi*), the Nevada Blue (*Polyommatus golgus*) and the Spanish Brassy Ringlet (*Erebia hispania*), as well as endemic races of butterfly species that are more widespread, such as the Spanish Argus (*Aricia morronensis ramburi*) and the Nevada Grayling (*Pseudochazara hippolyte williamsi*).

Threats to Mountain Wildlife

These days, many of Spain's characteristic high-altitude animals and plants are so well adapted to life among the peaks that they are unable to survive anywhere else. They are effectively stranded on 'islands' amid a sea of inhospitable lowland habitat, and if threatened by either natural or human-induced factors they have nowhere to go.

The Pyrenean subspecies of Spanish Ibex (*Capra pyrenaica pyrenaica*), locally known as the *Bucardo*, is a case in point. Although the *Bucardo* was once widely distributed throughout the Pyrenees, by the beginning of the 20th century hunting pressure and habitat loss had backed it into a corner of high Aragón. Despite the declaration of the Ordesa National Park in 1918, a combination of unsuitable habitat, genetic inbreeding, disease and competition with the Southern Chamois conspired to push this animal over the brink. By 1990 only ten individuals remained in the wild, and in 1998 the last known female was killed by a falling tree.

THE ATLANTIC DOMAIN

Subject to year-round Atlantic depressions, the northern and western reaches of Spain – that is, Galicia, Asturias, Cantabria and much of the País Vasco – are for the most part verdant, rain-washed lands where the Euro-Siberian climax vegetation typically comprises deciduous broadleaved forests dominated by the European Beech (*Fagus sylvatica*) and oaks (*Quercus* spp.).

Most deciduous trees possess large leaves with a thin cuticle and many stomata, designed for maximum photosynthetic output. Although this enables the trees to grow at a prolific rate, the down side is that levels of transpiration are also very high, with water constantly being lost through the stomata. Given the abundant rainfall of the Atlantic zone, for most of the year sufficient water can be obtained through the roots, but come winter, when the soil water is often frozen, the trees are at risk of desiccation. The solution is simple: at the onset of cold weather in the autumn, when light levels decrease and photo-synthesis is impaired, deciduous trees lose their leaves and enter a resting state.

Bare limbs are less likely to accumulate heavy loads of snow that might break more fragile branches, while the trees' cell sap also becomes more concentrated in winter, thus lowering its freezing point and reducing frost damage to soft tissues. At the same time, new buds are produced that are protected from the winter cold by leathery scales. When

BELOW Pyrenean Oaks form forests in both sub-Atlantic and sub-Mediterranean regions of Spain, usually on siliceous soils..

and Mountain and Scots Pines (*Pinus uncinata* and *P. sylvestris*) occur in the high Pyrenees and northern Sistema Ibérico, attractively mixed with beeches in the renowned Selva de Irati in Navarra. Where light levels are high, beeches and oaks may be accompanied by the Ash (*Fraxinus excelsior*) and Field Maple (*Acer campestre*), with Small-leaved and Large-leaved Limes (*Tilia cordata* and *T. platyphyllos*) being present on base-rich soils, the Wych Elm (*Ulmus glabra*) near rivers, and the birch *Betula alba* close to the tree-line. Smaller trees include the Hazel (*Corylus avellana*), Rowan (*Sorbus aucuparia*), Whitebeam (*S. aria*) and Wild Cherry (*Prunus avium*), as well as evergreens such as the Yew (*Taxus baccata*) and Holly (*Ilex aquifolium*).

The fruits of these trees provide a valuable winter food resource for the many creatures inhabiting the Atlantic forests.

ABOVE A superb example of a mixed European Beech and European Silver-fir forest in the Selva de Irati, Navarra.
OPPOSITE The northern flanks of El Moncayo (2,313 m), in the Sistema Ibérico, harbour an isolated enclave of beech woodland.

favourable conditions return in spring, the trees leap into action, physiologically speaking, producing new branches, leaves and flowers.

Canopy Trees

On the whole, the Pedunculate Oak (*Quercus robur*) is the dominant canopy species on deep, fertile soils in the valley bottoms, especially near the coast, although few forests of this nature are to be found in Spain today, having been largely replaced with pastures, meadows and eucalyptus plantations. The Fragas do Eume, in Galicia, is one of the best remaining Spanish examples of this woodland type.

The European Beech and Sessile Oak (*Quercus petraea*) tend to prefer lighter soils at greater altitude, while the Pyrenean Oak (*Q. pyrenaica*) is more typical of south-facing slopes on siliceous bedrock. Some of the best-preserved Atlantic beech woods occur in Somiedo in Asturias, Saja–Besaya in Cantabria and Señorío de Bértiz in Navarra, with Sessile Oaks a feature of the Asturian Bosque de Muniellos. The forest of Izki, in the País Vasco, is one of the largest expanses of Pyrenean Oak woodland in Spain.

Natural coniferous woodlands – the climax vegetation under colder climatic regimes in northern and central Europe – are by and large absent from Spain's Atlantic domain, although extensive tracts of the European Silver-fir (*Abies alba*)

Spring-flowering Ground Flora

It has been calculated that less than 2 per cent of sunlight reaches the forest floor in a mature beech forest in summer, although oaks typically display a rather less dense canopy. Because of this, many herbaceous woodland plants commence growth as soon as temperatures start to rise after the winter, often with the help of energy provided by underground storage organs, so that they can flower and set seed before the trees are in full leaf. Thus, after the sombre hues of winter, the onset of spring sees the Spanish Atlantic forests adorned with colourful carpets of Wood and Yellow Anemones (*Anemone nemorosa* and *A. ranunculoides*), Rue-leaved Isopyrum (*Isopyrum thalictroides*), Hepatica (*Hepatica nobilis*), Green Hellebore (*Helleborus viridis*), Pinnate Coralroot (*Cardamine heptaphylla*), Hollow-root (*Corydalis cava*), Primroses and Oxlips (*Primula acaulis* and *P. elatior*), Tuberous Comfrey (*Symphytum tuberosum*), Pyrenean Squill (*Scilla liliohyacinthus*), Dog's-tooth-violets (*Erythronium dens-canis*), Lily-of-the-Valley (*Convallaria majalis*), Ramsons (*Allium ursinum*) and the exquisite Angel's-tears (*Narcissus triandrus*). In addtion, one of the most characteristic beech-wood plants of northern Spain is the parasitic Purple Toothwort (*Lathraea clandestina*), which does not need light to grow as it satisfies its nutritional requirements by tapping into the roots of the trees.

By midsummer, when the tree canopy is fully developed, only the most shade-tolerant flowering plants are able to bloom. These include the Foxglove (*Digitalis purpurea*), the eye-catching toadflax *Linaria triornithophora*, Purple Lettuce (*Prenanthes purpurea*), Herb-Paris (*Paris quadrifolia*) and

ABOVE The poisonous alkaloid muscarine was formerly extracted from the Fly Agaric to destroy insects, hence its common name.

Martagon Lily (*Lilium martagon*) – and even they prefer woodland margins and clearings within the forest. By contrast, many ferns, especially those whose fronds fan out over a large area, are able to tolerate extremely low light levels. Among them are the distinctive Hart's-tongue Fern (*Phyllitis scolopendrium*),

BELOW The Martagon Lily is also sometimes known as the Purple Turk's Cap Lily, on account of its distinctive flower shape.

Oak Fern (*Gymnocarpium dryopteris*), Lady-fern (*Athyrium filix-femina*), Male-fern (*Dryopteris filix-mas*), Narrow Bucklerfern (*D. carthusiana*), Lemon-scented Fern (*Lastraea limbosperma*) and Soft and Hard Shield-ferns (*Polystichum setiferum* and *P. aculeatum*).

Saprophytes

Northern Spain's densest, most Stygian beech woods and conifer forests harbour a unique community of saprophytic herbs, many of which lack chlorophyll and thus cannot photosynthesize, instead procuring their nutrients from humus and decaying leaf litter in the surface layers of the soil. To do this, the plant's roots must be infected with a mycorrhizal fungus, in a symbiotic relationship from which both parties appear to benefit. From the plant's point of view, the presence of the fungus enables the roots to take up nutrients more efficiently, while the fungus profits by having somewhere to live.

True saprophytes such as the Bird's-nest Orchid (*Neottia nidus-avis*) and Yellow Bird's-nest (*Monotropa hypopitys*) – both of which have a dense tangle of roots with a large surface area to enable the fungus to operate at maximum efficiency – have no chlorophyll whatsoever. Other species, for example the wintergreens (family Pyrolaceae), are only partially saprophytic, also possessing some chlorophyll in their leaves and stems, and sometimes even in the flowers. In Spain, Palegreen, Common, Serrated and enchanting One-flowered Wintergreens (*Pyrola chlorantha*, *P. minor*, *Orthilia secunda* and *Moneses uniflora*) are found principally in coniferous forests in the northern and central reaches.

Perhaps the most enigmatic of the Spanish forest saprophytes, however, is the Ghost Orchid (*Epipogium aphyllum*), so named because of its unpredictability. Even in known localities, several decades may pass without a single flowering spike putting in an appearance. Despite being distributed across much of Europe, the Ghost Orchid is a very rare plant indeed; in Spain it is confined to European Beech and European Silverfir woods in the central Pyrenees, with an outlying population in the Sierra de Cebollera (La Rioja).

Fungi, of course, are saprophytes par excellence, and Spain's Atlantic forests are home to an enormous number of species, the fruiting bodies (mushrooms and toadstools) of which are produced mainly in spring and autumn. Among the most colourful are the lilac-tinged Amethyst Deceiver (*Laccaria amethystina*) and Wood Blewit (*Lepista nuda*), the egg-yolk-yellow *Tricholoma sulphureum*, the cautionary red cap of the Sickener (*Russula emetica*) and that favourite perch of cartoon gnomes, the Fly Agaric (*Amanita muscaria*).

The Forest Food Chain

The Atlantic forests are home to a diverse range of animals, all of which are inextricably linked by the forest food chain.

Woodland Butterflies and Moths

Many butterfly larvae feed exclusively on woodland plants, be they herbs, shrubs or trees, even though the adults tend to hang out in flowery glades – where sunshine raises their body temperature to a point where they might become active – in search of essential supplies of nectar. Violets (*Viola* spp.) are the chosen larval food plant of fritillaries in the genus *Argynnis*, while the Wych Elm is favoured by the caterpillars of Large Tortoiseshells (*Nymphalis polychloros*) and White-letter Hairstreaks (*Satyrium w-album*). Similarly, the larvae of the White Admiral (*Limenitis camilla*) feed on honeysuckles (*Lonicera* spp.), while those of the Duke of Burgundy Fritillary (*Hamearis lucina*) prefer Primroses (*Primula acaulis*) and Cowslips (*P. veris*). Many members of the family Satyridae select grasses as their larval host plant, including one of Europe's rarest butterflies, the Woodland Brown (*Lopinga achine*).

Even so, the total biomass of butterfly caterpillars fades into insignificance when compared to that of the moth larvae, some of which have even managed to acquire a taste for tough, bitter beech leaves, among them the Tau Emperor (*Aglia tau*), Lobster Moth (*Stauropus fagi*), Tawny Prominent (*Harpyia milhauseri*) and Brindled Beauty (*Lycia hirtaria*). Moths whose larvae feed on the foliage of deciduous oaks are legion, with some of the more memorable species being the December Moth (*Poecilocampa populi*), Oak Beauty (*Bison strataria*), Scalloped Oak (*Crocallis elinguaria*), Oak Hawkmoth (*Marumba quercus*), Lesser Puss Moth (*Cerura erminea*) and Black Arches (*Lymantria monacha*), plus the Dark Crimson Underwing (*Catocala sponsa*), Merveille du Jour (*Dichonia aprilina*) and a host of other noctuids.

Vertebrates of the Atlantic Forest

Because adult moths of different species are on the wing all year round, Spain's Atlantic forests are favoured hunting grounds for a number of bats (order Chiroptera, see also page 133), notably Whiskered and Bechstein's Myotis (*Myotis mystacinus* and *M. bechsteinii*), and the Brown Long-eared Bat (*Plecotus auritus*), as well as Nathusius' Pipistrelle (*Pipistrellus nathusii*) and the Barbastelle (*Barbastella barbastellus*).

Butterflies and moths represent only a very small fraction of the vast array of Atlantic deciduous forest invertebrates, which together provide a comprehensive menu for creatures higher up the food chain. Invertebrates that inhabit the leaf litter and rotting wood are consumed by forest-floor amphibians and reptiles such as Fire and Golden-striped Salamanders (*Salamandra salamandra* and *Chioglossa lusitanica*), Agile

RIGHT, TOP Silver-washed Fritillaries (*Argynnis paphia*) depend on nectar sources in woodland rides and clearings.

RIGHT, CENTRE The feathered antennae of the male December Moth can detect the scent of unmated females from several hundred metres.

RIGHT, BOTTOM A cold-tolerant species of montane woodlands, the Barbastelle is one of Europe's most endangered species of bat.

WOODPECKERS

These are archetypal forest birds (family Picidae). Almost all of the 200-odd species known to science possess short legs and strong-clawed toes arranged in a zygodactylous manner – that is, two pointing forwards and two backwards – as well as stiff, wedge-shaped tails that act as a prop when perched, providing a third point of contact against the vertical trunk for better balance and to support the weight of the bird.

Woodpeckers typically nest in holes in trees, excavating a cavity by repeatedly hammering the trunk with their hard, chisel-tipped beaks. Spongy structures within the bones of the skull act as 'shock absorbers' during this activity to prevent damage to the brain. In most woodpeckers, vocal communication is more or less limited to a series of alarm calls, with territorial declarations made by the rapid drumming of the beak against resonant trunks, each species drumming at a slightly different frequency.

ABOVE Middle Spotted Woodpeckers rear four to seven young that fledge in just three weeks.

The Black Woodpecker (*Dryocopus martius*) – by far the largest of the seven Spanish members of the Picidae – is found almost exclusively in the deciduous and coniferous forests of the Cordillera Cantábrica and Pyrenees. Sometimes measuring more than 50 cm from head to tail,

it is instantly recognizable by its funereal black plumage, which is relieved only by the male's vivid red crown (in the female it is reduced to a red patch on the nape). Black Woodpeckers feed primarily on the larvae and pupae of wood-boring beetles, impaling the insects on their pointed and barbed, protractile tongue, while smaller, hard-bodied insects are trapped by the tongue's sticky coating of salivary-gland secretions.

The four Spanish representatives of the genus *Dendrocopos* are distinguished by their pied plumage and red markings on the head and/or belly. The Great Spotted Woodpecker (*D. major*) is widespread in a range of habitats in Spain and other parts of Europe, but the White-backed Woodpecker (*D. leucotos*) is an essentially Eastern European species, represented in Spain by an outlying population (subspecies *D. l. lilfordi*) of 60–70 pairs in the mixed European Silver-fir and European Beech woods of Navarra. The mainly Central European Middle Spotted Woodpecker (*D. medius*) is more or less confined to the Cordillera Cantábrica in Spain, where it favours mature broadleaved forests, while the Lesser Spotted Woodpecker (*D. minor*) occurs in old deciduous woodlands across Spain, albeit with a markedly disjunct distribution.

Frogs (*Rana dalmatina*) and Bocage's Wall Lizards (*Podarcis bocagei*), as well as by small mammals like Common and Millet's Shrews (*Sorex araneus* and *S. coronatus*), Common and Iberian Moles (*Talpa europaea* and *T. occidentalis*), Western Hedgehogs (*Erinaceus europaeus*) and Bank Voles (*Clethrionomys glareolus*).

Similarly, the abundant supply of plant-eating insects is the nutritional foundation on which a whole host of forest songbirds raises its young. Because the dense foliage precludes the use of sight, male passerines generally declare their territories vocally. Each species has a distinctive song that both attracts females and warns rival males that its territory is already occupied. On spring mornings, the Atlantic woodlands echo with the liquid voices of myriad songbirds, but later in the year, when the chicks are almost fully grown, the forests are strangely silent. The females of these birds are often rather drab, the better to remain concealed from predators while sitting on the nest. Forest birds employ a variety of feeding techniques so

there is little competition between different species. Short-toed and Eurasian Treecreepers (*Certhia brachydactyla* and *C. familiaris*) and Eurasian Nuthatches (*Sitta europaea*) extract invertebrates from crevices in the bark with their long, thin beaks. Acrobatic titmice (family Paridae) hang precariously from the ends of branches, picking insect larvae from the leaves. Spotted and Pied Flycatchers (*Muscicapa striata* and *Ficedula hypoleuca*) prefer to trap insects on the wing, launching themselves time and again from a favoured perch, often on the edge of the wood, while Eurasian Blackbirds (*Turdus merula*) and Eurasian Woodcocks (*Scolopax rusticola*) forage in the leaf litter, the longer bills of the latter enabling them to probe deeply in search of earthworms.

While some of the more characteristic Atlantic forest insectivorous birds – the Tree Pipit (*Anthus trivialis*), Common Redstart (*Phoenicurus phoenicurus*), Garden Warbler (*Sylvia borin*) and Pied Flycatcher – migrate south for the winter to avoid the scarcity of available food, predominantly seed- or plant-eating species such as Eurasian Bullfinches (*Pyrrhula pyrrhula*) and Citril Finches (*Serinus citrinella*) are able to remain in these woodlands all year round. Others expressly visit the Atlantic domain at this time of year, taking advantage of the rich food supply therein. Flocks of Bramblings (*Fringilla montifringilla*) travel south from their Arctic breeding grounds to gorge themselves on beechmast, while Redwings (*Turdus iliacus*) and Fieldfares (*T. pilaris*) do likewise to feed on the succulent fruits of trees such as the Rowan, Holly and Yew.

As Red Squirrels (*Sciurus vulgaris*) are active throughout the winter, retreating to snug cavities in trees only during the worst weather, they spend much of the autumn collecting and storing food, particularly hazelnuts. By contrast, Western Hedgehogs and Garden and Edible Dormice (*Eliomys quercinus* and *Glis glis*) opt out of winter altogether by hibernating – that is, they enter a deep sleep in which their metabolic rate is reduced to a minimum, surviving on fat reserves accumulated during the autumn. Although they do not truly hibernate, Spanish Brown Bears (*Ursus arctos*) become lethargic between December and March. During this time their body temperature and pulse rate drop only marginally, and warmer spells encourage them out into the open.

Small birds are preyed on by Northern Goshawks (*Accipiter gentilis*) and Eurasian Sparrowhawks (*A. nisus*). These very agile birds of prey are characterized by their short, broad wings for acceleration to maximum velocity in the space of a few wing-beats, and long mobile tails that enable them to twist

ABOVE In Spain, the Eurasian Treecreeper is confined to deciduous and coniferous forests in the mountains of the north.

BELOW Northern Goshawks may rear up to six chicks in one brood, although three or four is the norm; they fledge after 5–6 weeks.

through the trees in pursuit of their prey. As its name suggests, the Eurasian Sparrowhawk preys mainly on small passerines, but the more substantial Northern Goshawk has a predilection for Eurasian Magpies (*Pica pica*), Eurasian Jays (*Garrulus glandarius*) and Carrion Crows (*Corvus corone*), as well as an occasional small mammal.

Several species of owl also hunt and breed in the Atlantic forests, feeding mainly on small mammals such as mice, voles and shrews. Some, like the Little Owl (*Athene noctua*), venture out during the day, but generally speaking owls are at their most active at dawn and dusk. Owls possess enormous eyes that are situated at the front of the head for superlative binocular vision, and compared to many other birds they have well-developed external ears. Because their primary wing feathers are fringed with fine down, owls can swoop down on their prey in almost complete silence, normally seizing it by the head with their powerful toes and long, curved talons. The most characteristic Atlantic forest species are Tawny and Long-eared Owls (*Strix aluco* and *Asio otus*), with Tengmalm's Owl (*Aegolius funereus*) confined to dense conifer forests in the Pyrenees in Spain.

Small arboreal mammals such as Red Squirrels and Garden and Edible Dormice provide food for acrobatic predators such as Beech and Pine Martens (*Martes foina* and *M. martes*), although these opportunistic mustelids will eat almost anything, including fruit and honey.

Cryptic Camouflage

During the day, owls hide away in the trees, camouflaged by their cryptically coloured plumage. The mottled feathers of a Tawny Owl are almost invisible against the bark of a tree, while Scops Owls (*Otus scops*) and Long-eared Owls both possess tufts of feathers resembling ears on the tops of their heads. These can be erected when the birds are resting, helping to break up the outline of the head and thus render them less visible to a sharp-eyed goshawk.

Not surprisingly, ground-nesting forest birds have also evolved plumage that helps them to escape detection, particularly the females, which are veritable 'sitting ducks' for much of the spring. For example, although male Capercaillies (*Tetrao urogallus*) are bold, black creatures, the females are barred and speckled in such a way as to blend in perfectly with the leaf litter and debris of the forest floor. Similarly, nocturnal Eurasian Nightjars (*Caprimulgus europaeus*) and crepuscular Eurasian Woodcock spend the daylight hours resting on branches or the ground, flawlessly camouflaged against the bark or dead leaves.

Among the mammals, young Wild Boar (*Sus scrofa*) sport a series of longitudinal stripes, while Roe Deer (*Capreolus capre-*

LEFT, ABOVE While they are incubating their eggs on the forest floor, female Eurasian Nightjars need to be perfectly camouflaged.

LEFT, BELOW Long-eared Owls occur throughout Spain, but are nowhere common, with an estimated population of just 5,000 pairs.

olus) fawns have spotted backs, both sets of markings rendering their owners virtually invisible against the sun-dappled forest floor and permitting the mothers to leave their offspring in relative safety while they themselves go in search of food.

Atlantic Grasslands and Heaths

During the millennial reign of the Atlantic forests, thick, fertile soils have accumulated beneath their canopy. Since Neolithic times, however, humans have gradually cleared the woodland to make way for pasture, hay meadows and arable land, creating a highly diverse mosaic of natural and semi-natural habitats where plants and animals more typical of open country are able to flourish alongside the forest element.

The traditionally managed hay meadows of northern Spain are among the most floristically rich Atlantic grasslands in the world, with an invertebrate fauna to match. Orchids and butterflies abound here, reaching their zenith in the Picos de Europa, where the centuries-old agricultural system employing native breeds of cattle remains largely intact.

Birds that hunt in open country but breed in forested habitats or scrub – for example Short-toed and Booted Eagles (*Circaetus gallicus* and *Aquila pennata*), Eurasian Buzzards (*Buteo buteo*) and Red-backed Shrikes (*Lanius collurio*), are also in their element here.

ABOVE The semi-natural hay meadows of the Picos de Europa harbour more than 600 species of vascular plant.

At greater altitude, close to the natural tree-line, forest clearance has produced extensive pastures and heathlands, the latter dominated by a closed canopy of ericaceous species such as the Ling (*Calluna vulgaris*), Bell Heather (*Erica cinerea*) and Spanish and Tree Heaths (*E. australis* and *E. arborea*), interspersed with various shrubby, yellow-flowered legumes of the genera *Genista*, *Cytisus* and *Ulex*.

This habitat is occupied by a rather specialized assemblage of breeding birds, including the Northern Harrier (*Circus cya-* neus), Grey Partridge (*Perdix perdix*), Bluethroat (*Luscinia svecica*), Whinchat (*Saxicola rubetra*) and Yellowhammer (*Emberiza citrinella*), and by the endemic Broom Hare (*Lepus castroviejoi*), first described in 1977 and unique to the Cordillera Cantábrica.

THE MEDITERRANEAN REALM

By far the largest part of mainland Spain, as well as the Balearic archipelago in its entirety, lies within the Mediterranean climatic zone. With a long history of human occupation, however, the thick evergreen forests that represent the climax vegetation are a thing of the past. They have largely been replaced by scrub, *dehesas*, dry pastures and a diverse assemblage of crop lands ranging from olive groves and vineyards to extensive dry cereal cultivations, although these secondary communities are by no means lacking in wildlife interest.

To the south of the Atlantic zone, beyond the influence of the oceanic weather systems, a Mediterranean climate prevails. This is characterized by a pronounced drought during the summer months, when the lack of rain is accentuated by high temperatures. Because of their high levels of transpiration, deciduous trees find it hard to cope with this lack of water in summer. They are therefore largely replaced by evergreen species – either broadleaves or conifers – in both peninsular Spain and the Balearic Islands.

On the whole, Mediterranean vegetation is dominated by sclerophyllous, evergreen trees and shrubs; that is, those that possess small, leathery leaves with a thick cuticle and stomata that are able to partially close up during very hot weather, thus regulating levels of transpiration when water is at a premium. Physiological activity is low during the summer, with most growth taking place during the spring and autumn rains. Although evergreen, the leaves of these trees and shrubs have a limited lifespan, but instead of all falling in the autumn, as in deciduous species, they are shed and replaced a few at a time throughout the year.

In the sub-Mediterranean zone that lies on the southern flanks of the Cordillera Cantábrica, semi-deciduous trees such as Pyrenean and Lusitanian Oaks (*Quercus pyrenaica* and *Q. faginea*) are commonplace, with the Downy Oak (*Q. humilis*) occupying a similar band in the southern Pyrenees. The leaves of these so-called marcescent species die in autumn, but instead of falling to the ground they remain on the tree until well into the winter, close to the new budding season. Their leaves are smaller and more leathery than the leaves of the truly deciduous trees, but not as tough as those of the sclerophyllous species.

For the most part, however, the broadleaved forests within Spain's Mediterranean climatic zone are dominated by the Western Holm Oak (*Q. ilex* ssp. *ballota*) on dry, sunny slopes and by the Cork Oak (*Quercus suber*) where the soils are more humid, particularly on north-facing slopes and in the west of the country. In the east of the region, especially in very dry habitats on limestones or coastal sands, these broadleaved oaks are replaced by forests of native conifers, in particular the Aleppo Pine (*Pinus halepensis*).

Mediterranean Broadleaved Forests

In the best-preserved Mediterranean broadleaved forests, as for example on north-facing slopes in the Monfragüe National Park (Extremadura), Cork and Lusitanian Oaks may be accompanied by the Montpellier Maple (*Acer monspessulanum*) and Strawberry Tree (*Arbutus unedo*) in the canopy. Here the shrub layer is represented by a dense tangle of Lusitanian and Tree Heaths (*Erica lusitanica* and *E. arborea*), Myrtle (*Myrtus communis*), Mediterranean Buckthorn (*Rhamnus alaternus*), Turpentine Tree (*Pistacia terebinthus*), Wild Jasmine (*Jasminum fruticans*), *Phillyrea angustifolia*, Wild Olive (*Olea europaea* var. *sylvestris*) and Laurustinus (*Viburnum tinus*). Where sufficient light penetrates, the spring ground flora is rich in bulbous species such as the Hoop-petticoat Daffodil (*Narcissus bulbocodium*), Wild Tulip (*Tulipa sylvestris* ssp. *australis*), Star-of-Bethlehem (*Ornithogalum umbellatum*), Tassel Hyacinth (*Muscari comosum*) and Lange's and Dense-flowered Orchids (*Orchis langei* and *Neotinea maculata*).

Further south, western Andalucía is home to one of the world's largest Cork Oak forests, Los Alcornocales. Maintained by high-humidity weather systems from the Atlantic, the canopy is dominated by Cork Oaks, with semi-deciduous Algerian Oaks (*Quercus canariensis*) growing in damp, shady valleys, Lusitanian and Western Holm Oaks on base-rich outcrops, and stands of Pyrenean Oak on north-facing slopes on the sandstones of the Sierra de Aljibe. Lianes creep up through the trees in search of light, notably the Common Smilax (*Smilax aspera*) and Virgin's Bower (*Clematis cirrhosa*). In addition, the hot, humid microclimate of the deepest ravines provides a refuge for remnants of the evergreen cloud forests that clothed much of southern Europe in the Tertiary period. Here the Bay (*Laurus nobilis*), Alder Buckthorn (*Frangula alnus* ssp. *baetica*) and *Rhododendron ponticum* ssp. *baeticum* cast a deep shade that favours myriad ferns, notably the curious *Psilotum nudum*, found only here in mainland Europe, and the semi-tropical *Christella dentata* in its only Spanish locality.

OPPOSITE, ABOVE Cork Oak bark is harvested every 8–12 years, then the year is painted on the trunks; these trees were stripped in 2000.
OPPOSITE, BELOW In the herbicide-free arable lands of Mediterranean Spain, Common Poppies and Cornflowers often outnumber the crop.

ABOVE French Lavender is one of the most characteristic shrubs of Spain's *dehesas*, *maquis* and *garrigue*.

Maquis and Garrigue

The importance of the Mediterranean forest in preventing soil erosion cannot be overstated, primarily because rain rarely falls directly on the ground. Remove the canopy, however, and the topsoil quickly gets washed away by the torrential storms that are so common in the Mediterranean region, particularly on steep slopes. Not surprisingly, trees find it almost impossible to recolonize these impoverished soils, and it is a sad truth that following centuries of timber extraction, grazing and burning, much of Mediterranean Spain is today clothed with secondary scrub formations known as *maquis* and *garrigue*, with only scattered fragments of the primeval forest persisting in the most remote corners of the peninsula.

Generally speaking, *maquis* is a dense, evergreen scrub from 1 to 3 m tall. On impoverished siliceous soils in the western Sierra Morena, for example, *maquis* communities are monopolized by white-flowered Gum, Sage-leaved, Narrow-leaved and Poplar-leaved Cistuses (*Cistus ladanifer*, *C. salviifolius*, *C. monspeliensis* and *C. populifolius*). These are interspersed with the pink-flowered *C. crispus* and Spanish Heath (*Erica australis*), yellow legumes such as *Genista hirsuta* and *Pterospartum tridentatum*, and the purple-flowered French Lavender (*Lavandula stoechas*).

By contrast, on calcareous soils, *maquis* is usually dominated by the Holly Oak (*Quercus coccifera*), Lentisc (*Pistacia lentiscus*), Rosemary (*Rosmarinus officinalis*) and pale-pink-flowered Grey-leaved Cistus (*Cistus albidus*), with elements such as *Cistus clusii*, *Erica multiflora*, Mediterranean Coriaria (*Coriaria myrtifolia*) and Shrubby Globularia (*Globularia aly-*

pum) being particularly characteristic of eastern Spain and the Baleares.

In the Mediterranean region, the chiefly tropical family Rafflesiaceae is represented by two fleshy parasitic species in the genus *Cytinus*, both of which lack chlorophyll and obtain their nutrients exclusively from the roots of cistuses and other shrubby members of the Cistaceae. In Spain, the pinkish-flowered *C. ruber* parasitizes only the Grey-leaved Cistus, while the yellowish *C. hypocistis* is less host-specific, attacking a wide range of white-flowered cistuses, sun-roses (*Halimium* spp.) and rock-roses (*Helianthemum* spp.).

The more open *garrigue* community represents one step further in the degradation of the Mediterranean forest. Rarely exceeding half a metre in height, it is particularly common on limestone bedrock in the east of the peninsula and on the Balearic Islands. A diverse range of shrublets can be found here, particularly on calcareous soils. These are usually evergreen and often spiny, and may contain aromatic oils to deter browsing creatures. On the Balearic island of Mallorca, for example, limestone *garrigue* on the Artà Peninsula is dominated by majestic clumps of the grass *Ampelodesmos mauritanica*, often accompanied by the Dwarf Fan Palm (*Chamaerops humilis*) and interspersed with low-growing mounds of Balearic endemic shrubs such as *Astragalus balearicus*, *Dorycnium fulgurans*, Balearic St John's -wort (*Hypericum balearicum*) and *Teucrium subspinosum*. The spring and autumn rains stimulate the flowering of a diverse assemblage of annuals, as well as prompting many species with underground storage organs (geophytes) into bloom. Rosy and Hairy Garlics (*Allium roseum* and *A. subhirsutum*), Naked Man Orchids (*Orchis italica*) and the magnificent Dragon's Mouth (*Helicodiceros muscivorus*) appear in spring, with Sea Squills (*Drimia maritima*) flowering in autumn and *Crocus cambessedesii* right through the winter.

Dehesas

In south-western Spain, many of the larger trees of the ancient forests – mainly the evergreen Western Holm and Cork Oaks, but also the semi-deciduous Lusitanian Oak – were spared, creating a savannah-like wood–pasture known as *dehesa* across vast tracts of undulating terrain. The original *dehesas* date back to the 10th century, with around 4 million hectares still present today, mostly in Extremadura and Andalucía in Spain, and in the Portuguese Alentejo, where they are called *montados*. The system was designed with extensive livestock rearing in mind, to provide winter grazing for the merino sheep brought in by the Moors, as well as for several native breeds of cattle. Summer grazing for the livestock tends to be located in nearby montane habitats, although some flocks of sheep still undertake a biennial transhumance right across Spain to the verdant pastures of the Cordillera Cantábrica, traditionally on foot along the *Cañadas Reales* (royal drovers' roads), but more often by lorry today.

The canopies of the remaining trees are pruned so that they acquire a characteristic umbrella-like shape. This is intended both to cast maximum shade in order to avoid soil desiccation, and to optimize acorn production, to provide food for the free-range Iberian black pigs that forage here in the autumn. The prunings themselves were traditionally used to produce charcoal, although today this custom is almost obsolete. By contrast, the practice of stripping the bark from the trunk and major branches of the Cork Oaks every 8–12 years is still a major industry in this part of Iberia, generating approximately 90 per cent of the world's annual cork harvest.

Dehesas are periodically ploughed and cultivated with cereals, more to maintain the extensive pasture lands by curtailing the invasion of scrub than for the grain yield. Their botanical interest is greatest several years after this event, when

ABOVE A flock of merino sheep arrives at its summer pastures in the Cordillera Cantábrica in the traditional manner: on foot.
BELOW Free-range Iberian Black Pigs, much valued for their succulent meat, forage in the *dehesas* of the Sierra de Aracena.

perennial herbaceous species have had time to recolonize the sward from surrounding areas. Among the most eye-catching spring flowers in the *dehesa* are the Palmate Anemone (*Anemone palmata*), Western Peony (*Paeonia broteri*), *Dianthus lusitanus*, Purple Viper's-bugloss (*Echium lycopsis*), Angular Solomon's-seal (*Polygonatum odoratum*) and several species of orchid, notably the Sawfly Ophrys (*Ophrys tenthredinifera*) and Bug Orchid (*Orchis coriophora*), while the September rains bring delicate bulbs such as the Autumn Narcissus (*Narcissus serotinus*) and Autumn Snowflake (*Leucojum autumnale*) into bloom.

Mediterranean Conifers

As their leaves are for the most part reduced to cylindrical, grooved needles, with the stomata able to close almost completely in dry periods to reduce water loss, conifers take over where the soils of the Mediterranean region are so dry that the sclerophyllous oaks cannot survive. Generally speaking, conifer seeds germinate best where high levels of light reach the forest floor, so they are also particularly common where the existing vegetation has been removed by clearing or fire.

Four species of pine occur in Mediterranean Spain, particularly in the east, where nowadays they are restricted to the driest, most impoverished habitats, having been replaced on richer soils by extensive Wild Olive (*Olea europaea*) groves. The widespread Aleppo Pine (*Pinus halepensis*) has an essentially eastern Spanish distribution, extending from the foothills of the Pyrenees to the southern Spanish coast, while the more frost-tolerant Black Pine (*P. nigra* ssp. *salzmannii*) has a more montane distribution within Mediterranean Spain. Sandy coastal soils, by contrast, are the stronghold of Stone and Maritime Pines (*Pinus pinea* and *P. pinaster*). However, as all the Spanish pines have been widely planted – for timber, to stabilize sandy soils, for harvesting resin in the case of the Maritime Pine and for the edible kernels of the Stone Pine – their natural distribution is rather uncertain.

Other native conifers of these Mediterranean lands include the junipers, of which only the Spanish Juniper (*Juniperus thurifera*) is a tree, forming open woodlands in more continental parts of the peninsula. The more shrubby Prickly, Common and Phoenician Junipers (*J. oxycedrus*, *J. communis* ssp. *hemisphaerica* and *J. phoenicea*) and Savin (*J. sabina*) are widespread in the shrub layer, especially under pines or in secondary *maquis*. The Barbary Arbor-vitae (*Tetraclinis articulata*) is a small coniferous tree with a western Mediterranean distribution. In Spain it occurs only on dry, sunny slopes in the coastal ranges near Cartagena (Murcia), while the three Spanish

LEFT, ABOVE Bug Orchids get their name from their foetid, bedbug-scented flowers, although the Spanish forms tend to be more fragrant.
LEFT, BELOW Tapping Maritime Pines for their resin is no longer carried out on a commercial scale, but the practice persists in remote areas.

species of the genus *Ephedra* all prefer calcareous soils in the eastern half of the peninsula, although the Joint-pine (*E. fragilis*) extends westwards through Andalucía into the Portuguese Algarve.

One of the largest expanses of natural pine forest in Mediterranean Spain occupies the high limestone plateaux of the Serranía de Cuenca. It is characterized by Black Pines over a sparse understorey of the Common Juniper, Barberry (*Berberis vulgaris*), *Genista scorpius*, Box (*Buxus sempervirens*) and *Lavandula latifolia*. The Aleppo Pine forests in the Cabrera National Park, of the Balearic archipelago, overlie a rather different community, dominated by the Phoenician Juniper, Joint-pine, Tree Spurge (*Euphorbia dendroides*), Cneorum (*Cneorum tricoccon*), Lentisc, the Spanish endemic buckthorn *Rhamnus ludovici-salvatoris*, Wild Olive and *Phillyrea angustifolia*.

Perhaps the most distinctive conifer of the region, however, is the Spanish Fir (*Abies pinsapo*), which is thought to have been pushed south by the advancing ice sheets of the Pleistocene epoch, then stranded when they retreated. Today only about 1,200 ha of these *pinsapares* remain in Spain, confined to the mountains of Cádiz and Málaga, with further extensions occurring in the western Rif (North Africa). Perhaps the best-known tract of Spanish Fir forest in Spain is that of the humid, north-facing slopes of the Sierra del Pinar, in the Grazalema Biosphere Reserve. Some of the oldest trees, thought to be more than 500 years old, reach a height of about 30 m and have trunks almost a metre in diameter. So little light reaches the forest floor at any time of year that the ground flora is restricted to just a few extremely shade-tolerant species such as the Stinking Hellebore (*Helleborus foetidus*), the peony *Paeonia coriacea*, Stinking Iris (*Iris foetidissima*) and Red Helleborine (*Cephalanthera rubra*).

ABOVE The sandy soils of the Doñana National Park support fabulous stands of mature Stone or Umbrella Pines.

Animals of the Mediterranean

Spain's Mediterranean habitats are of enormous significance to wildlife. The broad canopy of the oaks provides the ideal nesting habitat for many raptors, notably Cinereous Vultures (*Aegypius monachus*), Spanish Imperial Eagles (*Aquila adalberti*, see box, page 127) and Black-shouldered Kites (*Elanus caeruleus*), as well as for a wealth of smaller species such as Woodchat Shrikes (*Lanius senator*), Spotless Starlings (*Sturnus unicolor*) and Iberian Azure-winged Magpies (*Cyanopica cooki*).

The dense scrub of the region, by contrast, harbours numerous warblers, particularly those of the genus *Sylvia*. These include Subalpine, Sardinian and Western Orphean Warblers (*S. cantillans*, *S. melanocephala* and *S. hortensis*), with the Balearic Warbler (*S. balearica*), which is endemic to the archipelago of the same name, being perhaps the most noteworthy of the bunch.

In winter, the *dehesas* of the region are of prime importance for Common Cranes (*Grus grus*), which head south from their northern European breeding grounds to feed on the abundant acorn crop. The most recent censuses indicate that about 150,000 birds winter in Spain each year.

The European Rabbit (*Oryctolagus cuniculus*) plays a key role in the Mediterranean ecosystem, featuring extensively in the diet of two of the region's most emblematic predators, the Iberian Lynx (*Lynx pardinus*, see box, page 47) and the Spanish Imperial Eagle. Since the middle of the last century, however, with the arrival first of Myxomatosis and later Rabbit

ABOVE European Rabbits provide food for many top predators in the Mediterranean realm.

ABOVE The majestic Cinereous Vulture is Spain's largest bird of prey, with a wingspan of up to 295 cm.

Hemorrhagic Disease, Spain's rabbit population has been virtually wiped out in many areas, with disastrous results higher up the food chain. Many bats are particularly associated with the Mediterranean woodlands and *dehesas*, including Mehely's and Mediterranean Horseshoe Bats (*Rhinolophus mehelyi* and *R. euryale*), the Greater Mouse-eared Bat (*Myotis myotis*), Kuhl's and Savi's Pipistrelles (*Pipistrellus kuhli* and *P. savii*), Leisler's Bat (*Nyctalus leisleri*), Greater Noctule (*N. lasiopterus*) and Serotine (*Eptesicus serotinus*).

The Iberian Hare (*Lepus granatensis*), which is unique to the peninsula, is also abundant here, as is the Garden Dormouse (*Eliomys quercinus*). Typical larger mammals include the Small-spotted Genet (*Genetta genetta*) and Egyptian Mongoose (*Herpestes ichneumon*), both of which are thought to have been introduced from North Africa in ancient times, as well as the Wild Boar (*Sus scrofa*) and Red Deer (*Cervus elaphus*).

Butterflies of Spain's Mediterranean Lands

Diversity is just as high in the invertebrate groups, with a number of eye-catching butterflies inhabiting Mediterranean habitats. Three exquisite members of the Papilionidae – the Spanish Festoon (*Zerynthia rumina*), Swallowtail (*Papilio machaon*) and Spanish Swallowtail (*Iphiclides feisthamelii*) – can be found pretty well throughout Spain in spring, with the essentially tropical Monarch (*Danaus plexippus*) and Plain Tiger (*D. chrysippus*) occurring very locally along the Mediterranean coast.

The equally attractive Two-tailed Pasha (*Charaxes jasius*) is confined to areas where its larval host plant – the Strawberry Tree – is abundant, occurring mainly along the eastern seaboard of Spain, on the Balearic archipelago and in Andalucía. Although it is a bivoltine species, flying in late spring and again in the autumn, the second generation is usually much more prolific than the first.

The diminutive Chapman's Green Hairstreak (*Callophrys avis*) is another species whose caterpillars feed on the Strawberry Tree. This spring-flying western Mediterranean butterfly is distinguished from the much more widespread Green Hairstreak (*C. rubi*) in having eyes bordered with red rather than white.

Many typical butterflies of Spain's Mediterranean habitats have an essentially Iberian distribution in Europe, notably the Provence Orange Tip (*Anthocharis euphenoides*), Green-striped White (*Euchloe belemia*), Aetherie and Spanish Fritillaries (*Melitaea aetherie* and *Euphydryas desfontainii*), Western, Spanish and Iberian Marbled Whites (*Melanargia occitanica*, *M. ines* and *M. lachesis*), Striped Grayling (*Hipparchia fidia*) and Spanish Gatekeeper (*Pyronia bathseba*). Among the quasi-endemic lycaenids are Provence and Spanish Purple Hairstreaks (*Tomares ballus* and *Laeosopis evippus*) and Lorquin's Blue (*Cupido lorquinii*), with Panoptes and Spanish Chalkhill Blues (*Pseudophilotes panoptes* and *Lysandra albicans*) being confined to the peninsula.

IBERIAN LYNX

Without a doubt, the best-known vertebrate of Spain's Mediterranean habitats is the Iberian or Pardel Lynx (*Lynx pardinus*), which since 2002 has had the unfortunate distinction of being labelled 'the world's most endangered feline'. Although it occupied large expanses of the Iberian Peninsula in the past, as a top predator the Iberian Lynx has never been common. However, its decline over the past 20 years has been nothing short of spectacular, with the world population collapsing from an estimated 1,100 individuals in 1988 to just 120 breeding animals in 2005; it is now probably extinct in Portugal.

Although its scarcity is in large part due to the decline of its principal prey species, the rabbit, there is no doubt that the plethora of infrastructure projects – motorways, high-speed rail links and large dam schemes – that has taken place since Spain joined the European Union is equally to blame, continually disrupting the lynxes' habitat and cordoning them off into smaller and smaller enclaves.

Today only two populations of Iberian Lynx remain, both in Andalucía: in the Sierra de Andújar, central Sierra Morena, and in the Doñana National Park and environs. The two are separated by some 250 km of hostile, largely humanized habitats traversed by major roads and railways and present-ing a formidable barrier to communication between the two nuclei. The Doñana population, estimated at 20–24 breeding animals, is on shaky ground genetically, and although 15 cubs were born in 2006, juvenile mortality is high; 19 individuals were killed on the roads here between 2000 and 2006. The future of the Andújar nucleus is a little brighter, however, with some 60–80 breeding animals occupying one of the best-preserved and least-disturbed expanses of Mediterranean forest, *dehesa* and scrub in Europe. In 2006, no less than 58 cubs were added to this population. Because of the greater number of individuals concerned, the Andújar population is less likely to enter a genetic bottleneck, and indeed, there are plans to relocate individuals from here to Doñana to give that nucleus a new lease of life.

In recent years, a successful captive breeding programme has been initiated with the aim of releasing animals into other areas of suitable habitat from 2010 onwards. The immediate concern, however, is to achieve and maintain a nucleus of around 60 breeding animals to safeguard the Iberian Lynx from extinction.

BELOW Carnivore par excellence, the Iberian Lynx is undoubtedly top of the food chain in Spain's Mediterranean ecosystems.

ARID LANDS AND PSEUDOSTEPPES

The world's arid habitats are defined by their very low levels of precipitation and high levels of evaporation. True deserts generally receive less than 100 mm of precipitation each year, arid lands under 250 mm and semi-arid regions between 250 and 500 mm. Much of the centre of the Iberian Peninsula – far beyond the reach of humid winds originating in the Atlantic or Mediterranean – can be considered semi-arid, with even drier enclaves occurring in the Ebro Depression, La Serena (Extremadura) and the extreme south-eastern corner, in Almería and Murcia, although there are no true deserts in Spain.

Broadly speaking, Spain's heartland, the *Meseta*, is a bleak, windswept plateau split into northern and southern reaches by the Sistema Central. Although largely covered with forest in the dim and distant past, millennia of felling, burning and grazing by the burgeoning human population – aided and abetted by the lack of rainfall – have given rise to vegetation resembling that of the *stepj* of Eastern Europe and much of central Asia. These true steppes are climatic climax communities that are dominated by grasslands, but for the most part the man-made 'pseudosteppes' of Spain are secondary communities, comprising a mosaic of extensive arable habitats, grazing lands and low woody vegetation known as *garrigue* (see page 42).

Steppe Grasslands

Only in very arid or saline enclaves, where trees are unable to survive, do grass-dominated 'steppe' communities occur naturally in Spain. The most characteristic steppe grasses are the False Esparto (*Stipa tenacissima*), Mediterranean Needle-grass (*Stipa capensis*) and Albardine (*Lygeum spartum*), all of which can tolerate low levels of rainfall, high summer temperatures and strong winds. Their fibrous roots form a dense mat in the upper layers of the soil, effectively trapping any moisture that might fall, and their long, fine leaves are arranged vertically so as not to shade one another, allowing for maximum photosynthesis during favourable periods, but avoiding overheating from excess insolation.

Windy conditions facilitate the pollination of grass flowers, but these species do not rely entirely on seed production, also reproducing vegetatively by means of subterranean rhizomes. During periods of drought, the aerial parts of these grasses might die, but growing points at the bases of the leaves remain active throughout the lives of the plants, thus enabling them to withstand fire and grazing.

Although vast tracts of grassland dominated by *Stipa lagascae*, *S. parviflora* and Albardine once covered the deep, gypsum-rich soils of the Ebro Depression, over the years they have been gradually ousted by the cultivation of cereals. Today the best remaining examples can be found in the arid enclaves of the Bardenas Reales in Navarra, and Belchite and Los Monegros in Aragón. Here they are interspersed with a gypsophilous com-

munity characterized by the rock-rose *Helianthemum squamatum*, the crucifer *Lepidium subulatum* and the pink-flowered restharrow *Ononis tridentata*, all of which are Afro-Iberian endemics, together with *Gypsophila struthium* and the wormwood *Artemisia herba-alba*.

Salt Steppes

In particularly arid areas of Spain, where evaporation exceeds precipitation, the predominant water movement is upwards through the soil, drawing mineral salts with it and creating high levels of salinity near the surface. These so-called salt steppes tend to have a very distinctive flora, with obvious links to the coastal plant communities of Spain (see page 68), and are typically dominated by succulent, halophytic members of the goosefoot family (Chenopodiaceae).

One of Spain's most typical inland salt steppes is the Saladares del Guadalentín, in Murcia, where the main fleshy chenopods are the Shrubby Sea-blite (*Suaeda vera*), Common Glasswort (*Sarcocornia fruticosa*), *Anabasis articulata* and *Halocnemum strobilaceum*, together with succulent members of other families such as the Golden-samphire (*Inula crithmoides*, family Compositae) and *Lycium intricatum* (family Solanaceae). Other characteristic halophytes here are the sea-heath *Frankenia corymbosa*, as well as three Spanish endemic sea-lavenders, *Limonium caesium*, *L. cossonianum* and *L. delicatulum*.

Chenopods representative of saline soils in the Ebro Depression are the Shrubby Sea-blite, Purple Glasswort (*Salicornia ramosissima*), *Salsola vermiculata*, *Microcnemum coralloides* and *Halopeplis amplexicaulis*, interspersed with other fleshy leaved plants, notably *Aizoon hispanicum* (family Aizoaceae) and *Peganum harmala* (family Zygophyllaceae). Further south, the Almerían salt steppes boast a classic array of chenopods such as *Anabasis articulata* and *Hammada articulata*, plus the saltworts *Salsola genistoides*, *S. oppositifolia* and the Spanish endemic *S. papillosa*. The roots of these chenopods are often parasitized by the curious Cynomorium

OPPOSITE The extraordinary eroded gypsum landscape of the Bardenas Reales, in the Ebro Depression, southern Navarra.

ABOVE Oleander flowers provide a valuable source of nectar for the insects of arid habitats..

BELOW Although Dwarf Fan Palms can develop trunks several metres high, grazing pressure in many areas arrests their growth.

(*Cynomorium coccineum*), which produces fleshy, dark red inflorescences rather like upside-down skittles, as well as by the eye-catching yellow-flowered spikes of Cistanche (*Cistanche phelypaea*).

Stony Steppes

In Almería – one of the most arid regions of Spain, and indeed Europe – broad swathes of inhospitable, rocky terrain host a climax vegetation dominated by the endemic gorse *Ulex canescens*, the greenweed *Genista spartioides*, Maytenus (*Maytenus senegalensis*), spiny hummocks of *Ziziphus lotus*, *Periploca laevigata* ssp. *angustifolia* and Dwarf Fan Palm (*Chamaerops humilis*), although centuries of human occupation have relegated this unique community to the most remote areas today. Similar formations can be found further east at Calblanque, embellished by the largest Spanish enclave of the juniper-like small tree known as the Barbary Arbor-vitae (*Tetraclinis articulata*), an essentially North African member of the cypress family (Cupressaceae).

Plant Adaptations

All arid habitats are characterized primarily by the lack of water available to living organisms. As a response to these conditions, the xerophytic vegetation of these habitats has developed a series of morphological and physiological adaptations in order to survive. Roots – all-important in the uptake of water – develop either as an extensive network just below the surface, as in the case of the steppe grasses, or as enormously long taproots capable of exploiting the subterranean water supply, as exhibited by the pink-flowered Oleander (*Nerium oleander*) and feathery-leaved tamarisks (*Tamarix* spp.; seven native species in Spain), both of which are a familiar sight along seasonal watercourses in the Iberian Peninsula.

Most evergreen plants of arid regions have very small leaves, whose reduced surface area is designed to cut down on the amount of water lost by transpiration. In the case of the Barbary Arbor-vitae, for example, the leaves are little more than tiny scales. For the same reason, thick, waxy cuticles are often the order of the day, and in many cases the stomata are confined to the margins of the leaves, which are often rolled under so as to curtail air movement and maintain humid conditions.

In order to prevent overheating, some plants are able to orient their leaves close to the vertical, so that the fierce noonday sun hits only the edges, while many plants of arid lands have grey or whitish leaves to reflect the sun's rays. In the driest habitats, especially in saline conditions, many plants have succulent leaves and stems, with enlarged parenchyma cells in the tissues, which allow the plants to store water. The cell sap of these species contains a higher concentration of salts than the surrounding soil to facilitate the absorption of water by osmosis. Other halophytes such as sea-heaths (*Frankenia* spp.) and

ABOVE The inhospitable-looking steppe grasslands in the Desierto de Tabernas, in Almería, in fact support a wealth of wildlife.

sea-lavenders (*Limonium* spp.) are able to excrete excess salt through the epidermal cells, so that the plants appear to be covered with a fine powder, which again may help to reflect the sun's rays.

In the most extreme cases, the leaves have been lost altogether, or are reduced to small spines, as in the New World cacti and the succulent spurges of the Canary Islands (see page 78). In these species photosynthesis must be carried out by the stems, which are therefore green. Such stems often bear longitudinal pleats that allow them to expand, concertina-fashion, to store water whenever it is available, for subsequent use in times of drought. In mainland Spain, perhaps the most distinctive plants of this nature are two species of *Caralluma* in the milkweed family (Asclepiadaceae): *C. europaea*, which grows in southern Almería, and *C. munbanya*, from neighbouring Murcia. In both cases the tiny leaves fall very early, leaving just a fleshy, angular stem topped with a cluster of relatively large, star-shaped flowers.

For the most part, trees cannot grow in arid regions as there simply is not enough water to sustain them. The perennial shrubs may be evergreen, which has the advantage of allowing them to start photosynthesizing the moment sufficient moisture becomes available, or deciduous, shedding their leaves in times of drought to prevent water loss, but with the drawback of having to produce new leaves before growth can recommence. Among the herbaceous species, geophytes, which die back completely during dry periods, storing energy in bulbs and tubers under the ground, are common. They include the

winter-flowering lily *Androcymbium europaeum*, unique to Almería, and the Afro-Iberian endemic *Lapiedra martinezii* (family Amaryllidaceae), which blooms during the autumn.

Annual plants are a particular feature of arid lands throughout the world, many producing seeds that can remain viable for decades, waiting patiently until suitable conditions return. In many instances, the seeds are coated with germination inhibitors that prevent them from sprouting unless sufficient rain falls to wash these chemicals away, in this way ensuring that enough water will be available for the plants to complete their life cycles. When this happens, previously barren tracts of sand and stone burst into bloom, sometimes overnight; an event that is often referred to as the 'flowering of the desert'. Large, brilliantly coloured blooms – often heavily scented – are a feature of such annuals. They are designed for maximum appeal to pollinators, and set seed within a matter of days to guarantee the survival of the species until the rains return.

Arable 'Weeds'

Although a large part of the *Meseta* has been converted to agriculture, the extensive cereal fields, pastures, vineyards and olive groves are by no means lacking in botanical interest. On the whole, they are farmed in a low-intensity manner using the bare minimum of pesticides and fertilizers, and thus harbour an immense diversity of eye-catching annual 'weeds' that

particularly the spectacular purple-flowered *Nigella papillosa*, Cow Basil (*Vaccaria hispanica*), Large Blue Alkanet (*Anchusa azurea*), the delicate Venus's Looking-glass (*Legousia hybrida*), pink-and-white or yellow spikes of *Bellardia trixago*, Corn Marigold (*Chrysanthemum segetum*) and tall yellow-and-white Crown Daisies (*Chrysanthemum coronarium*).

Annual members of the poppy family (Papaveraceae) are particularly at home in cereal fields. They range from bright red Prickly and Rough Poppies (*Papaver argemone* and *P. hybridum*), both with bristly seed capsules, to the vivid yellow *Hypecoum* spp., with their curious, bivalve-like flowers. Violet Horned-poppies (*Roemeria hybrida*) have deep mauve flowers, Red Horned-poppies (*Glaucium corniculatum*) are distinguished by their reddish-orange flowers marked with blackish patches at the bases of the petals, while the low-growing Spiked Fumitory (*Platycapnos spicata*) and a whole host of trailing fumitories (*Fumaria* spp.; 24 in Spain) present elongated heads of zygomorphic flowers in a range of pinks.

Animals of Arid Lands

Although no living creature can survive without water, Spain's arid lands are home to a rich and diverse faunal community, the members of which display a range of both morphological adaptations and behavioural strategies to help them avoid the heat and conserve their body fluids.

Many invertebrates and reptiles never drink at all, obtaining all of their water requirements from their food, but mammals travel considerable distances to find water, usually at dusk or dawn, when temperatures are less fierce than during the day. European Rabbits (*Oryctolagus cuniculus*), Algerian Hedgehogs (*Atelerix algirus*) and Algerian Mice (*Mus spretus*) are largely nocturnal, escaping the heat of the day in subterranean burrows, where the temperature is lower and the humidity is much higher, partly as a consequence of the animal's own respiration.

Steppe Birds

The majority of steppe birds have evolved physiological mechanisms that reduce the need to drink regularly, although Black-bellied and Pin-tailed Sandgrouse (*Pterocles orientalis* and *P. alchata*) are known to visit water bodies regularly, possibly because their diets consist principally of seeds with a very low water content. In addition, male sandgrouse possess specialized barbed belly feathers that act like sponges; by immersing themselves in water they are able to soak up liquid to transport back to their chicks.

The very sparseness of the vegetation in Spain's arid lands encourages movement on foot, while its low height allows the birds to feed – on insects or seeds, as the case may be – without needing to take to the air. As flight is considered to be more costly in energetic terms than walking or running, this is a distinct advantage in arid habitats where food might be scarce at

ABOVE Common Poppies are perhaps the most widespread and abundant annual plants of disturbed soils.
BELOW The stunning purple flowers of the love-in-a-mist *Nigella papillosa* can measure 7 cm in diameter.

thrive in disturbed habitats. Whole fields of wheat, oats or barley might be coloured red by Common Poppies (*Papaver rhoeas*) or blue by Cornflowers (*Centaurea cyanus*), or sometimes even hazed pink by Corncockles (*Agrostemma githago*).

Other attention-grabbing Spanish arable weeds include the pheasant's-eyes (*Adonis* spp.), which can be either red- or yellow-flowered, several species of love-in-a-mist (*Nigella* spp.),

certain times of year. Insectivorous birds and those that consume small vertebrates, such as Eurasian Thick-knees (*Burhinus oedicnemus*), tend to have relatively long legs that both raise their eyes to a better vantage point for spotting prey, and enable them to move fast in pursuit of mobile quarry. By contrast, birds such as sandgrouse that feed primarily on seeds tend to have much shorter legs, so that their eyes are closer to the ground in order to detect their food. Many steppe species are gregarious, foraging in small flocks and taking it in turns to remain vigilant; for the most part the birds remain silent while feeding to avoid attracting unwanted attention.

Most feeding activity occurs in the early morning, when temperatures are more moderate than later in the day, as do courtship displays and song flights that establish territories, although the birds might resume these activities in the late evening. Dawn at the onset of spring in the Spanish steppes is heralded by the glorious song of myriad passerines, especially Calandra, Thekla, Crested, Short-toed and Dupont's Larks (*Melanocorypha calandra*, *Galerida theklae*, *G. cristata*, *Calandrella brachydactyla* and *Chersophilus duponti*). In the steppes, where perches out of reach of predators are rare, an aerial song flight is obviously far less risky than a terrestrial one, while timing it for dawn to some extent avoids the attentions of birds of prey, many of which must wait for thermals to develop before starting their day.

By contrast, aerial courtship displays for heavy-bodied species such as Great and Little Bustards (*Otis tarda* and *Tetrax tetrax*) are simply out of the question due to the excessive amount of energy they would consume. Instead male bustards tend to strut their stuff in open, relatively exposed areas, where the approach of predators is easy to detect.

In a land without trees, most birds are obliged to nest on the ground within easy reach of predators, so cryptic camouflage of the adults, eggs and chicks is of the utmost importance. The overall plumage of most steppe birds is generally sand-coloured, often broken up by darker stripes or mottling, the better to blend in with the specific features of the terrain they inhabit. Their eggs and chicks are similarly camouflaged, and in many species the egg markings vary according to the specific nesting habitat selected.

Bustards, Eurasian Thick-knees and sandgrouse make little attempt to build nests, simply laying their eggs in shallow depressions. The chicks of these non-passerine species are nidifugous: down-covered when they hatch and able to run after their parents within a few hours. In general, both sexes incubate the eggs, although in polymorphic species such as sandgrouse the more distinctively marked males tend to do so at

BELOW The eggs and nidifugous chicks of the Eurasian Thick-knee are just as well camouflaged as the adults.

ABOVE Only male Ocellated Lizards (here the type subspecies *lepidus*) possess the distinctive blue 'eyes' along the flanks.

night or during the early morning and late evening, when the sun is low and they are less likely to be detected. Clutch size in nidifugous steppe birds tends to be small, and – more importantly for species that need to be constantly on the move – all the eggs hatch at the same time.

By contrast, steppe passerines such as larks and Tawny Pipits (*Anthus campestris*) construct similar cup-like nests to their tree-breeding relatives, possibly to provide their nidicolous chicks with protection both from overheating during the day and intense cold at night. In these species, incubation is almost entirely down to the cryptically coloured females. Nevertheless, the development of the chicks is extraordinarily rapid, and in most cases they are able to abandon the nest within a week or two of hatching.

The rich assemblage of invertebrates, small mammals and reptiles of the Spanish plains provides easy pickings for the country's smaller raptors such as Montagu's and Northern Harriers (*Circus pygargus* and *C. cyaneus*), Black-shouldered Kites (*Elanus caeruleus*) and Lesser Kestrels (*Falco naumanni*), while the magnificent Bonelli's Eagle (*Hieraaetus fasciatus*), which feeds primarily on medium-sized birds and mammals, is

particularly associated with arid and semi-arid habitats in south-eastern Spain.

Reptiles

Because they are cold-blooded and need to absorb heat from the sun in order to become active, many reptiles find Spain's hot, dry habitats very much to their liking, particularly Spur-thighed Tortoises (*Testudo graeca*, see also page 109) and Ocellated Lizards (*Timon lepidus*). In the arid south-eastern corner of mainland Spain, the normally bright-green Ocellated Lizard is represented by the race *T. l. nevadensis*, which is distinguished by its greyish-brown colouration. This undoubtedly enables it to blend in well with its surroundings and thus avoid detection by potential predators, notably Short-toed Eagles (*Circaetus gallicus*), Beech Martens (*Martes foina*) and Egyptian Mongooses (*Herpestes ichneumon*).

The Spur-thighed Tortoises of Almería and Murcia tend to be smaller than those that occur in less arid habitats elsewhere in Europe, the females rarely exceeding 21 cm in length and weighing around 2 kg, with the males often half as heavy. Because they feed primarily on vegetable matter, it stands to reason that Spur-thighed Tortoises are most active in spring and autumn, when the tender herbaceous plants produce new growth. They are often considered to be lethargic creatures, but studies have shown that in the breeding season the males are capable of travelling distances of a kilometre or more in a single day. The adult tortoise's heavy carapace and the leathery scales that cover the legs and head help to prevent dehydration, as well as providing valuable defence against predators, although the eggs and young are consumed by a whole range of carnivorous birds and mammals.

Invertebrates

The best-studied of Spain's continental arid lands is without a doubt Los Monegros, in the Aragonese sector of the Ebro Depression, where entomological surveys have assembled an inventory of more than 3,500 species since the end of the 1980s, dozens of them new to science. Beetles (order Coleoptera), with their hardened elytra (wing-cases), are particularly at home in Spain's arid lands, with more than 800 species having been recorded in Los Monegros (of a total of more than 10,000 in Spain, including the archipelagos).

Terrestrial, wingless species such as the darkling beetles *Akis genei*, *Pimelia villanovae*, *Blaps lethifera* and *B. lusitanica* (family Tenebrionidae) are hard-bodied, long-legged detritivores that spend much of the summer hanging around on the outskirts of anthills, feeding on the 'rubbish' thrown out by the occupants. By contrast, the 120-odd species of ground beetle (family Carabidae) that occur in Los Monegros tend to be more actively carnivorous, although some are phytophagous and others are carrion eaters.

Grasshoppers and crickets (order Orthoptera) are also abundant in arid lands, with about 65 species having been cited in Los Monegros. Although it is widely believed that grasshoppers and crickets are plant eaters, quite a number of the latter are in fact either carnivorous or feed extensively on carrion – particularly members of the family Tettigoniidae. This is obviously an advantage in extremely arid conditions, where plant material is scarce at certain times of year. The majority of orthopterans spend the winter in the egg stage, hatching in spring and passing through several nymphal stages before reaching maturity by the autumn. Of the 600 or so European species of grasshopper and cricket, more than half occur in Spain, including many endemics.

On the whole, orthopterans are stout, rather succulent insects that form a major part of the summer diet of steppe birds as diverse as Montagu's Harriers, Lesser Kestrels, Great and Little Bustards, European Rollers (*Coracias garrulus*) and Lesser Grey Shrikes (*Lanius minor*). Of necessity, cryptic camouflage is widespread, with species such as the Blue-winged Grasshopper (*Oedipoda caerulescens*) displaying an extremely varied range of colour forms according to the terrain it occupies. If by chance it should be detected, the vivid blue flashes in its wings are thought to startle the would-be predator, giving the grasshopper the opportunity to make good its escape.

Other orthopterans choose to secrete themselves among the vegetation, with several species having developed

ABOVE The rather soft-bodied scorpion *Buthus occitanus* avoids the heat of the day by hiding under rocks, emerging at night to hunt.
BELOW In order to avoid detection by predators, many grasshoppers are cryptically camouflaged.

extremely elongated heads and bodies that resemble plant stalks, as in the case of *Truxalis nasuta* and *Acrida turrita*, while the grasshopper *Mioscirtus wagneri* is almost exclusively associated with succulent halophytic vegetation and has a body pattern to match. The rare and endangered *Dericorys carthagonovae* is endemic to semi-desert habitats in Alacant, Murcia and Almería.

Some of the most voracious predators of badland invertebrates, however, are in fact other invertebrates, particularly fast-moving species such as the scorpion *Buthus occitanus*, the wolf spider *Lycosa fasciventris* and the tiger beetle *Cicindela maroccana*, to say nothing of *Scolopendra cingulata*, the largest European centipede, which may exceed 15 cm in length. Ant-lion larvae (for example those of *Myrmecaelurus trigrammus* and *Myrmeleon gerlindae* in Los Monegros) represent another threat to unwary invertebrates. These strong-jawed creatures construct conical 'pitfall' traps in loose sand and bury themselves at the bottom to wait patiently for unsuspecting ants and other small arthropods to lose their footing.

IBERIAN OIL BEETLES

The black-and-red Striped Oil Beetle (*Berberomeloë majalis*) – one of the largest of the European coleopterans, sometimes over 6 cm in length – is a typical species of dry habitats throughout the Iberian Peninsula. The herbivorous adults are often seen trundling about during the day, dragging their cumbersome abdomens behind them, but their young are not quite so innocuous. In spring, the female oil beetles excavate vertical burrows in loose soil in which to lay their eggs.

ABOVE The endemic Royal Oil Beetle is listed as Vulnerable in the Red Data Book of Spanish Invertebrates.

in the Iberian Peninsula) follow this rather hit-and-miss reproductive scenario, with the females laying huge numbers of eggs in an effort to ensure that at least one triungulin manages to locate a suitable host. As their name suggests, oil beetles are able to secrete a highly toxic, oily fluid, which is rich in a reddish substance known as cantharidin, from their joints when threatened. This serves to deter most predators, although hedgehogs and some birds appear to be immune.

The newly hatched, louse-like larvae, which are known as triungulins, head for the top of the nearest flower stem, where they lie in wait for solitary bees that are collecting pollen to stockpile for their young. Using their hooked legs, the triungulins hitch a lift back to the nest, where they proceed to devour the bee's eggs and grubs, before developing into much more maggot-like creatures that then eat their way through the hoard of pollen. When they have reached a certain size these larvae pupate in the burrow, emerging as adults the following spring.

All the soft-bodied oil beetles of the genera *Berberomeloë*, *Physomeloë* and *Meloë* (in total 18 species

Four rather scarce Iberian species of *Meloë* – *murinus*, *nanus*, *baudueri* and *ganglbaueri* – are almost entirely restricted to arid, steppe-like habitats. All are small, rarely more than 2–3 cm long and, unlike many other oil beetles, predominantly nocturnal, sheltering under stones to avoid the heat of the day.

The real jewel of the group, however, is the Royal Oil Beetle (*Berberomeloë insignis*), which is endemic to the badlands of Granada, Almería and Murcia. Although similar in size to Striped Oil Beetles, it can be distinguished from them by its all-black abdomen and the two large, blood-red patches on the back of its head.

Last but not least, a handful of butterflies have their only known European breeding colonies in Spain's arid lands. The diminutive Common Tiger Blue (*Tarucus theophrastus*) is confined to dry, rocky terrain in Almería and Murcia, as its distribution is limited to that of its larval host plant, the spiny shrub *Ziziphus lotus*, and of the ants that attend its caterpillars, *Crematogaster fuentei*.

The Greenish Black-tip (*Euchloe charlonia*) is known only from two widely separated arid enclaves in mainland Spain – the Hoya de Baza in Granada, and Los Monegros, in the Ebro Depression – as well as occurring on the eastern Canary Islands. Both the Desert Orange Tip (*Colotis evagore*), whose larvae feed principally on Capers (*Capparis spinosa*), and its close relative the Sooty Orange Tip (*Zegris eupheme*) are restricted to dry habitats in southern Andalucia.

LEFT Sooty Orange Tips can often be seen nectaring on their larval host plant, the Hoary Mustard (*Hirschfeldia incana*).

CONTINENTAL WETLANDS

Wetlands are among Europe's most vulnerable habitats, threatened by drainage to provide land for agriculture and building purposes, by over-exploitation of aquifers, by the damming of rivers and canalization of watercourses, and above all, by pollution. That said, Spain is home to a wide range of well-preserved wetlands, together supporting an exceedingly diverse flora and fauna.

Broadly speaking, continental wetlands can be divided into two principal types: lotic habitats are characterized by their running waters, namely springs, streams and rivers, while the still (standing) waters of lakes, ponds and bogs are classified as lentic habitats. Between both lotic and lentic habitats and their surrounding terrestrial ecosystems there exists a 'half-way house' that is often extraordinarily rich in plants and animals.

Aquatic Plants

Plants with submerged leaves must somehow obtain the gases they need for photosynthesis and respiration from the surrounding water rather than from the air. Because aquatic plants – often called hydrophytes – are not exposed to the drying effects of sun and wind they have no need for thick cuticles and tiny stomata through which to transpire, so gaseous exchange is possible over the whole surface of the underwater foliage. The submerged leaves of aquatic plants are often much divided in order to increase their surface area and thus maximize this interchange. In species whose large, floating leaves are exposed to the air, for example White and Yellow Waterlilies (*Nymphaea alba* and *Nuphar luteum*), these do in fact possess cuticles and stomata on their upper surfaces.

Because the surrounding water provides ample support, aquatic plants are also not obliged to develop the hard, woody tissues that terrestrial plants need to hold up their foliage. Instead, their stems and petioles are generally hollow, while the surrounding tissue – known as aerenchyma – contains many air-filled intercellular spaces, assisting with both buoyancy and gaseous exchange. These stems must also be very flexible, both to deal with buffeting by the current in rivers, and to allow plants with floating leaves to maintain them on the surface in water bodies where the level varies according to the

BELOW The endorheic Laguna de Gallocanta, in southern Aragón, is Spain's largest natural inland water body.

ABOVE During the spring snow-melt, the fast-flowing mountain streams of Benasque, in the Aragonese Pyrenees, become raging torrents.

season. Because some southern Spanish lagoons dry out completely at certain times of year, successful aquatic plants must have a strategy in hand to be able to survive until wet conditions return. Curiously, many of these strategies are similar to those utilized by plants of arid habitats. Some are dependent on underground storage organs, others die back to the base, where dormant buds can rapidly produce new growth when water levels rise once more, and yet others are annual species whose survival is entirely dependent on the production of seed. In terms of reproduction, most freshwater aquatic vascular plants operate in the same way as their terrestrial counterparts, producing wind- or insect-pollinated flowers that are hoisted above the surface of the water – be it still or flowing – often resulting in spectacular floral 'carpets' such as those of the water crowfoots (*Ranunculus* spp.).

Rivers

In their upper reaches, close to the headwaters, infant rivers are represented by small streams coursing down steep mountain slopes, often tumbling over waterfalls and rapids en route. These clean, fast-flowing waters are highly erosive, carving narrow, steep-sided valleys and generally deterring the growth of vegetation in the watercourse itself, although the margins may support a diverse assemblage of montane plants that prefer humid conditions.

In their middle reaches, rivers become much larger, swelled by the waters of numerous tributaries. Flatter terrain may permit a river to effect a meandering course, the margins of which are often flanked with thick galley forests.

Just before they reach the sea, where the gradient is barely perceptible, rivers tend to widen enormously and the flow rate decreases to the point where sediments eroded in the upper courses cannot be carried any further, sometimes creating a fan of deposits known as a delta.

The major factor influencing plant growth within the river itself is the speed of the current, with mountain torrents being virtually inimical to higher plants, but sluggish lowland rivers hosting a range of submerged and floating species. The composition of the flora of a mature river depends on factors such as the amount of dissolved oxygen present, water pH – itself determined largely by the bedrock – and turbidity, which affects the amount of light penetrating the water.

Submerged Aquatics of Lotic Systems

It stands to reason that in order to avoid being washed away, all riverine aquatic plants must have strong roots. Among the more characteristic species are the water crowfoots, with the Stream Water Crowfoot (*Ranunculus penicillatus*) being typical of fast-flowing, nutrient-rich watercourses, able to grow even in waterfalls, and Pond and Common Water Crowfoots (*R. peltatus* and *R. aquatilis*) more at home in oligotrophic rivers, where they might be accompanied by the Alternate-leaved Water-milfoil (*Myriophyllum alterniflorum*). Despite their vernacular names, some species of pondweed also occur in swift-running water – especially those with submerged linear leaves that can 'go with the flow', so to speak. They include the Loddon Pondweed (*Potamogeton nodosus*) and Opposite-leaved Pondweed (*Groenlandia densa*).

Fringing Vegetation

The margins of the middle and lower reaches of Spanish rivers, where the soil is waterlogged but the flow is barely perceptible, host an extremely diverse flora similar to that found fringing lentic water bodies. The basic building blocks of this marginal vegetation comprise stands of the Common Reed (*Phragmites australis*), Giant Reed (*Arundo donax*), bulrushes (*Typha latifolia*, *T. angustifolia* and *T. domingensis*), Branched and Unbranched Bur-reeds (*Sparganium erectum* and *S. emer-*

sum), club-rushes (*Schoenoplectus* spp.), Great Fen-sedge (*Cladium mariscus*) and a vast array of galingales (*Cyperus* spp.), sedges (*Carex* spp.) and rushes (*Juncus* spp.). More eye-catching elements include the Marsh Mallow (*Althaea officinalis*), Yellow and Purple Loosestrifes (*Lysimachia vulgaris* and *Lythrum salicaria*), Blue Water-speedwell (*Veronica anagallis-aquatica*), Water-plantain (*Alisma plantago-aquatica*) and Narrow-leaved Water-plantain (*A. lanceolatum*), Arrowhead (*Sagittaria sagittifolia*) and Yellow Flag (*Iris pseudacorus*).

Reed beds are home to one of the most diverse breeding bird assemblages in Spain. Typical denizens range from members of the heron family (Ardeidae) such as Great and Little Bitterns (*Botaurus stellaris* and *Ixobrychus minutus*), and Squacco and Purple Herons (*Ardeola ralloides* and *Ardea purpurea*) to the Water Rail (*Rallus aquaticus*) and Western Marsh Harrier (*Circus aeruginosus*).

Reed beds also provide suitable nesting habitats for many rather specialized small passerines, including the Great Reed

ABOVE Purple Herons typically construct their nests in the depths of impenetrable reed beds, out of reach of most predators.
LEFT, ABOVE Bulrushes are equally at home along the margins of large rivers and in a fringing belt around ponds and lakes.
LEFT, BELOW A Little Bittern stalks along the water's edge in search of prey, primarily of young fish, amphibians and insects.

Warbler (*Acrocephalus arundinaceus*), Eurasian Reed Warbler (*A. scirpaceus*), Cetti's Warbler (*Cettia cetti*), Moustached Warbler (*Acrocephalus melanopogon*), Savi's Warbler (*Locustella luscinioides*), Bearded Reedling (*Panurus biarmicus*) and Reed Bunting (*Emberiza schoeniclus witherbyi*).

With the exception of the Marsh Harrier and Bearded Reedling, which are absent from the Baleares, all of these species breed in good numbers in the vast S'Albufera de Mallorca reed bed, with noteworthy mainland examples of this habitat occurring around the Laguna de Pitillas, in Navarra, and in the Ebro Delta.

ABOVE Tamarisks, of which there are seven native species in Spain, are a characteristic component of Mediterranean riverine vegetation.

ABOVE Eurasian Golden Orioles are summer visitors to Spain, spending most of the breeding season in the high canopy of gallery forests.

Gallery Forests

In a pristine state, ribbon-like gallery forests – in Spain known as *sotos* – control a river's exuberance. The extensive root systems of the trees consolidate the banks, while the dense 'jungle' of undergrowth acts as a buffer against flooding when the river is in spate. Gallery forests often represent biogeographical islands of great species diversity amid veritable 'deserts' of arable land, and also represent corridors along which animals can migrate.

The exact composition of the gallery forest canopy depends on the size of the watercourse, how often it breaches its banks and the type of bedrock, as well as whether it occurs in the Atlantic or Mediterranean climatic zone. On base-rich soils in Mediterranean lands, the dominant trees are usually Small-leaved Elms (*Ulmus minor*) and White and Black Poplars (*Populus alba* and *P. nigra*), with the Narrow-leaved Ash (*Fraxinus angustifolia*) and Alder (*Alnus glutinosa*) being more typical of siliceous substrata. Along major rivers in the Atlantic zone, the Ash (*Fraxinus excelsior*) is often substituted for the Narrow-leaved Ash, the Aspen (*Populus tremula*) might replace the White Poplar and the Wych Elm (*Ulmus glabra*) is more common than the Small-leaved Elm.

Willows abound in gallery forests of both climatic zones, with White, Almond and Olive Willows (*Salix alba*, *S. triandra* and *S. elaeagnos*) being most typical of northern Spanish gallery forests, the Mediterranean Willow (*S. pedicellata*) occurring further south and *S. salviifolia* being unique to the western half of the Iberian Peninsula. Also typical of riverine woods in more Mediterranean climes are less lofty species such as tamarisks (*Tamarix* spp.), the Chaste Tree (*Vitex agnus-castus*), Oleander (*Nerium oleander*) and the shrubby *Flueggea tinctoria*, a member of the spurge family (Euphorbiaceae). Mountain streams are often fringed with shrubby willows, with *Salix cantabrica* being characteristic of northern Spain and *S. hastata* occurring in the Pyrenees and Sierra Nevada.

Among the emblematic birds of mature gallery forests such as the Soto de Buicio, on the River Ebro where it runs along the border of the País Vasco with La Rioja, are Eurasian Penduline Tits (*Remiz pendulinus*), which construct pouch-shaped nests lined with fluffy poplar seeds at the ends of slender branches, where they are out of reach of predators, and Eurasian Golden Orioles (*Oriolus oriolus*), the stunning yellow-and-black male birds of which are surprisingly difficult to detect among the sun-dappled foliage.

Still Waters

While most of the inland water bodies in the mountains of Spain are of glacial origin, some of the most important lakes on the *Meseta* and in the southern lowlands are endorheic. Notable examples include Fuente de Piedra and Gallocanta. These lagoons can only become established in flat-bottomed basins lined with impermeable soils. Small, rainwater-fed streams rising in the surrounding hills flow down into the depression, creating a shallow lagoon in the absence of any outlet. Where very low summer rainfall coincides with high levels of evaporation, these endorheic lagoons are highly seasonal and often markedly saline.

Still waters are the preferred habitat of free-floating hydrophytes – that is, those that are not rooted in the bottom sediments. Among the most characteristic members of this group are the diminutive duckweeds (family Lemnaceae), represented by three genera in Spain, all of which are capable of forming green 'carpets' on the surface of the water.

The 'leaves' – which are known as thalli – of Fat, Common and Least Duckweeds (*Lemna gibba*, *L. minor* and *L. minuta*) are roughly circular or oval, whereas those of the Ivy-leaved Duckweed (*L. trisulca*) are distinctly pointed and generally float just beneath the surface. In all cases each thallus is equipped with just a single root. The quasi-cosmopolitan Greater

ABOVE The glacial lake of La Ercina, set against a dramatic backdrop of limestone crags in the Picos de Europa National Park.

Duckweed (*Spirodela polyrhiza*) and *S. punctata*, by contrast, possess multiple roots per thallus, while roots are absent altogether from the sub-globose thalli of the Rootless Duckweed (*Wolffia arrhiza*).

Other carpet-forming floating plants are tiny ferns belonging to the family Azollaceae, notably *Azolla filiculoides*, *A. caroliniana* and *Salvinia natans*, all of which are introduced species originally native to subtropical America, and a number of rather scarce aquatic liverworts, namely the Purple-fringed Riccia (*Ricciocarpus natans*), Slender Riccia or Crystalwort (*Riccia fluitans*) and *Riella helicophylla*.

Glacial Lakes

Spain's largest glacial lake is that of Sanabria, in Zamora, and it covers 368 ha and is up to 50 m deep in places. Other notable examples can be found in the Aigüestortes National Park, in the Catalan Pyrenees, which encompasses more than 200 much smaller lakes, here known as *estanys*, as well as the chilly waters of Enol and La Ercina in the Picos de Europa National Park. Further south, the Peñalara massif, in the Sierra de Guadarrama just north of Madrid, houses more than 240 permanent and temporary glacial lakes and pools. Other lakes

ABOVE The distinctive, three-petalled flowers of the Lesser Water-plantain occur along the margins of still waters throughout Spain.

of note include the glacial water bodies of the Sierra Nevada and the Sierra de Urbión, in the Sistema Ibérico.

Typical rooted species with floating leaves of Spain's glacial lakes are Broad-leaved and Red Pondweeds (*Potamogeton natans* and *P. alpinus*), while the leaves of the related Long-stalked and Slender-leaved Pondweeds (*P. praelongus* and *P. filiformis*) all lie beneath the surface. These may be accompanied by other vascular hydrophytes such as the circumboreal crucifer Awlwort (*Subularia aquatica*), Spiked Water-milfoil (*Myriophyllum spicatum*), a number of water-starworts (*Callitriche* spp.), Floating Bur-reed (*Sparganium angustifolium*), Floating Water-plantain (*Luronium natans*), the grass *Antinoria agrostidea* and several species of *Isoetes* – related to the clubmosses and horsetails – notably the Quillwort (*Isoetes lacustre*) and Spring Quillwort (*I. echinosporum*).

The margins of the cold, clear waters of Spain's glacial lakes often sport a dense fringing belt of the Water Horsetail (*Equisetum fluviatile*), Bogbean (*Menyanthes trifoliata*) and various sedges and spike-rushes, typically Bottle and Bladder Sedges (*Carex rostrata* and *C. vesicaria*) and the Common Spike-rush (*Eleocharis palustris*). The Lesser Water-plantain (*Baldellia ranunculoides*) and the rare Spanish endemic *B. alpestris* may occur at the water's edge, along with the Lesser Marshwort (*Apium inundatum*), Marsh Speedwell (*Veronica scutellata*) and the loosestrife *Lythrum borysthenicum*.

Endorheic Lagoons

Perhaps the most noteworthy aquatics of Spain's seasonal, hyper-saline interior lagoons are the charophytes, sometimes referred to as stoneworts. These primitive plants are usually considered to be algae, even though many are distinctly branched and often heavily calcified, while their reproductive structures have close affinities with those of the bryophytes (mosses and liverworts). The seasonal lagoons of Villafáfila, in Zamora, harbour one of the richest charophyte assemblages in Spain, comprising the Foxtail Stonewort (*Lamprothamnium papulosum*), *Chara galioides*, Rough Stonewort (*C. aspera*), Bearded Stonewort (*C. canescens*), Fragile Stonewort (*C. globularis*) and Bird's nest Stonewort (*Tolypella nidifica*), *T. hispanica* and Clustered Stonewort (*T. glomerata*).

Aquatic higher plants that are able to tolerate high levels of salinity abound in both the endorheic and coastal lagoons of Spain, notably the quillwort *Isoetes velatum*, Rigid and Soft Hornworts (*Ceratophyllum demersum* and *C. submersum*), Beaked and Spiral Tasselweeds (*Ruppia maritima* and *R. cirrhosa*), *R. drepanensis*, Holly-leaved Naiad (*Najas marina*) and several species of horned pondweed (*Zannichellia* spp.). The marginal vegetation is typically composed of succulent halophytic chenopods and is very similar to that of Spain's inland salt steppes, intermixed with stands of the Sea Club-rush (*Bolboschoenus maritimus*), *Schoenoplectus litoralis* and various salt-tolerant rushes (*Juncus* spp.).

Although fish and amphibians are hard put to survive in the Spanish endorheic lagoons, salt-tolerant crustaceans and other aquatic arthropods abound, providing plentiful food for a wide range of birds.

It is no accident that Fuente de Piedra, Spain's largest endorheic water body, is home to one of the most prolific colonies of the Greater Flamingo (*Phoenicopterus roseus*, see also page 123) in Europe, which shares this habitat with nesting Pied Avocets (*Recurvirostra avosetta*), Black-winged Stilts (*Himantopus himantopus*) and Snowy or Kentish Plovers (*Charadrius alexandrinus*), plus huge numbers of waders during the winter and on passage. The Dark Spreadwing (*Lestes macrostigma*) is perhaps the most typical damselfly of Spain's endorheic lagoons.

Peat Bogs

Peat bogs are extremely wet habitats that develop best on nutrient-poor, typically siliceous soils. Although they are rare in the Iberian Peninsula, the finest Spanish peat bogs are situated in regions that receive the highest rainfall, occurring in scattered pockets in the Cordillera Cantábrica, Pyrenees and Sistema Central.

Among the most typical peat-bog plants are various species of bog-moss (*Sphagnum* spp.), of which more than 30 occur in Spain. *Sphagnum* leaves contain many hollow, porous cells that can soak up water from their surroundings, at the same time absorbing minerals. In active peat bogs, the *Sphagnum* plants grow at the tips and die back at the bases, the dead leaves decaying under anaerobic conditions to form peat.

The most characteristic vascular plants are Common and Hare's-tail Cottongrasses (*Eriophorum angustifolium* and *E. vaginatum*) and various rushes and sedges, notably the Spanish endemic *Carex durieui*, plus the Bog-sedge (*C. limosa*), Slender Sedge (*C. lasiocarpa*) and Lesser Tussock-sedge (*C. diandra*), all of which have a very localized distribution in Iberia.

A surprising richness of colour in the summer is provided by the Marsh Violet (*Viola palustris*), Bog Pimpernel (*Anagallis tenella*), Grass-of-Parnassus (*Parnassia palustris*), Hairy Stonecrop (*Sedum villosum*), Marsh Cinquefoil (*Potentilla palustris*), Starry Saxifrage (*Saxifraga stellaris*), Marsh Gentian (*Gentiana pneumonanthe*), Marsh Felwort (*Swertia perennis*), Lousewort (*Pedicularis sylvatica*), Alpine Bartsia (*Bartsia alpina*), Tofield's Asphodel (*Tofieldia calyculata*), Bog Asphodel (*Narthecium ossifragum*) and various insectivorous sundews and butterworts (see below). The Sierra Nevada peat bogs – the southernmost in Europe – are graced with Spanish endemics such as the gentian *Gentiana boryi*, the butterwort *Pinguicula nevadensis* and the speedwell *Veronica turbicola*.

Small pools within the bog might host aquatic species such as the quillwort *Isoetes velatum*, Least Water-lily (*Nuphar luteum* ssp. *pumilum*), Bogbean, Lesser Bladderwort (*Utricularia minor*, see page 64), Bog Pondweed (*Potamogeton polygonifolius*) and Floating Bur-reed.

The Viviparous Lizard (*Zootoca vivipara*) is particularly at home in the northern Spanish peat bogs, whether they are at sea level or at more than 2,400 m in the Pyrenees. Despite its name, in Spain this species is primarily oviparous, the females laying a single clutch of 4–7 eggs each summer. Nevertheless, the eggs remain inside the female for much longer than is usually the case for lizards, so that when the eggs are laid the embryos are in an advanced state of development, hatching just a month later. The diet of Viviparous Lizards consists of insects, spiders and other arthropods, as well as small snails, slugs and earthworms.

Insectivorous Plants

Although the majority of the world's insect-eating plants occur in tropical regions, Europe is also home to a number of these highly specialized 'carnivores', which tend to be found in nitrogen-deficient habitats such as peat bogs and calc tufa deposits. Although they also contain chlorophyll and are able to photosynthesize normally, these plants cannot obtain enough nitrogen from the soil to produce viable seed without resorting to alternative means.

RIGHT, ABOVE Pied Avocets feed by sweeping their slightly opened bills sideways through the surface sediments to trap invertebrates.

RIGHT, BELOW A member of the primrose family, the delicate Bog Pimpernel is also found in temporarily waterlogged habitats.

The tiny bladders – only 1–5 mm in diameter – are closed at one end by a 'trap door' surrounded by touch-sensitive, hair-like appendages that are positioned so as to guide prey to the entrance. An unsprung trap has concave sides on account of the partial vacuum within, ensuring that the door remains tightly sealed. The slightest touch of an aquatic creature on the trigger hairs is sufficient to break the tension, thus sucking both door and victim inside. Once the vacuum has been released, the door returns to its former position and digestion and absorption of the prey commences, carried out by enzymes secreted by glands lining the inside of the bladder.

The family Lentibulariaceae is also represented by nine species of butterwort (*Pinguicula* spp.) in Spain, four of which are endemic. These terrestrial herbs have very poorly developed root systems and basal rosettes of pale-green leaves that lie flat against the ground, the upper surfaces of which are greasy to the touch, hence the vernacular name. The 'greasiness' is due to a dense coat of glandular hairs, each tipped with a thick drop of mucilage, which is responsible for trapping small insects, while an underlying layer of sessile glands secretes enzymes to digest the prey. The zygomorphic flowers are long-spurred, five-lobed and range from deep purple through lilac to white.

One of the most spectacular members of the genus *Pinguicula* is the Large-flowered Butterwort (*P. grandiflora*), whose deep-purple flowers up to 25 mm across can be found in wet meadows and peat bogs in northern Spain, the Sierra de Guadarrama and the Sierra Nevada. Other acid-loving Spanish species include the Common Butterwort (*P. vulgaris*), from the northern half of Spain, and the Pale Butterwort (*P. lusitanica*), an essentially western Iberian species with tiny pale-pinkish flowers. By contrast, several uniquely Spanish butterworts occur only in wet calcareous habitats, notably *P. dertosensis* in eastern Spain, *P. vallisneriifolia* in the Sierras de Cazorla y Segura and nearby ranges, and *P. mundi*, which is known only from the Serranía de Cuenca, in Castilla–La Mancha.

ABOVE The insectivorous Large-flowered Butterwort grows in nitrogen-poor habitats on both acid and calcareous bedrock.

Two main strategies are utilized by Spanish insectivorous plants. The bladderworts (*Utricularia* spp.), as their name suggests, trap aquatic invertebrates by means of tiny ovoid bladders attached to the leaves or stems, while in the remaining genera – *Drosera*, *Drosophyllum* and *Pinguicula* – it is the sticky leaves that ensnare unwary insects.

Four species of *Utricularia* (family Lentibulariaceae) can be found in Spain, all of which are submerged aquatic plants with two-lipped, spurred yellow flowers that rise above the surface of the water on long, slender stalks. The most common species by far is the Bladderwort (*U. australis*), which is widespread in fresh and brackish waters across many of the Iberian wetlands, while the Greater Bladderwort (*U. vulgaris*) and the circumboreal Lesser Bladderwort prefer acid pools in the peat bogs of northern Spain. By contrast, the predominantly tropical *U. gibba* is restricted to sandy coastal lagoons located in south-western Iberia.

Sundews (family Droseraceae) are characterized by the long-stalked glandular hairs that cover the upper surfaces and margins of the leaves. The Afro-Iberian endemic Yellow Sundew (*Drosophyllum lusitanicum*) is a particularly eye-catching plant of dry siliceous soils in south-west Spain, its array of long, slender leaves giving it a distinctly spider-like appearance. The fabulous yellow, five-petalled flowers can be up to 5 cm in diameter, while the leaves are equipped with six longitudinal rows of reddish-tipped, stalked glands.

The three Spanish species of white-flowered *Drosera*, by contrast, are typical European peat-bog plants distinguished from one another principally by their leaf shape. The Round-leaved Sundew (*D. rotundifolia*), is the most widespread

species, occurring from sea level up to altitudes of more than 2,000 m, while Great and Oblong-leaved Sundews (*D. longifolia* and *D. intermedia*), both of which occur principally in northern Spain, have much narrower leaf-blades arranged on long stalks. All three species can be seen in the peat bogs of Izki, in the southern País Vasco.

Animals of Aquatic Habitats

Just as plants have evolved a variety of techniques by which to extract oxygen from the water, so have a number of animals. Fish are obviously the best-adapted aquatic vertebrates, quite unable to survive out of the water. Instead of possessing air-breathing lungs, fish have paired gills, each of which is made up of a series of blood-rich, flat, sheet-like structures (laminae) with an enormous surface area. Water enters the mouth and is expelled through the gill flaps, in between times passing over these laminae, where gaseous exchange is carried out. In addition, many fish are able to supplement this oxygen supply by 'breathing' through their skin, whereby oxygen enters the cells by a process of diffusion; some carbon dioxide is lost in the same way.

Amphibians

All Spanish amphibians have aquatic larvae. Newt and salamander larvae, sometimes called efts, possess feathery external gills to facilitate gaseous exchange, and are also able to 'breathe' through the skin. During metamorphosis, however,

ABOVE The round pupils of the Viperine Snake serve to distinguish it at a glance from the slit-pupilled vipers that it superficially resembles.

the adults develop air-breathing lungs, although skin breathing can still take place whenever they enter the water, particularly during the breeding season. By contrast, except in the very early stages, frog and toad tadpoles have internal gills. These are aerated by a stream of water that enters via the mouth and exits through an opening known as the spiracle that is positioned either on the belly or on the left flank.

Reptiles

Despite their poikilothermic tendencies, several species of reptile are particularly associated with Spanish wetlands. Grass and Viperine Snakes (*Natrix natrix* and *N. maura*) are both excellent swimmers and are rarely found far from water in Spain. Viperine Snakes in particular are experts at hunting underwater, using both scent and touch to locate their prey – principally small fish, amphibians and aquatic invertebrates – and can easily remain submerged for more than 15 minutes.

Southern Spanish rivers are often adorned with higgledy-piggledy stacks of terrapins of all sizes basking in the sun. Two species occur in Spain: the Spanish Terrapin (*Mauremys leprosa*) – a quasi-Afro-Iberian endemic otherwise known only from a few French populations – and the European Pond Terrapin (*Emys orbicularis*), the sole naturally occurring Old World representative of the essentially American family Emydidae, which is sparsely distributed across much of south-

ern and eastern Europe. Both are primarily carnivorous and are found in rivers and lakes throughout lowland Spain to altitudes of around 1,000 m, except for the most northerly reaches. Since they are fairly tolerant of saline waters, they also occur in coastal wetlands.

The Spanish Terrapin usually sports a series of yellowish or orange stripes on the sides of the neck, and has a fairly uniformly coloured shell, while the carapace of the European Pond Terrapin is generally marked with pale radial stripes, and the legs and neck are boldly speckled with yellow. Both of these species of terrapin have been known to attain lengths of about 25 cm, although most never reach more than 15 cm. Although primarily aquatic species, terrapins bury their eggs in soft, sunny substrata, often some distance from water. The newly hatched individuals are only 2–3 cm long and many are snapped up by terrestrial predators as they make their way to the nearest water body.

Birds

For the most part, avian adaptations to an aquatic existence are morphological rather than physiological. Ducks and geese (family Anatidae) are equipped with broadly webbed feet and thick, waterproof plumage, and although grebes (family Podicipedidae) have lobed rather than webbed toes, their feet are placed far back towards the rear of the body so as to facilitate diving, giving them a clumsy gait on land.

Grebes can spend an incredibly long time underwater, swimming with their wings held close to the body in pursuit of fish and aquatic invertebrates. As a defence against predators, grebe chicks are semi-nidifugous, leaving the nest early but then hitching a ride on the backs of the adults. Three grebe species breed regularly in Spain, with Great Crested and Little Grebes (*Podiceps cristatus* and *Tachybaptus ruficollis*) being widespread in inland waters.

The White-throated Dipper (*Cinclus cinclus*) also feeds primarily underwater, but is associated almost exclusively with lotic habitats. These rotund, chocolate-coloured birds often submerge themselves completely in their hunt for aquatic invertebrates, either walking along the river bed or swimming upstream. White-throated Dippers have particularly dense plumage and possess a broad membrane above the nostrils, which can be closed while they are underwater.

Many waders, storks and herons have disproportionately long legs, enabling them to feed in shallow water without immersing their bodies, while their long, spreading toes allow them to traverse soft ground without sinking. Similarly, the greatly elongated digits of the Purple Swamp-hen (*Porphyrio porphyrio*) are ideal for walking on rafts of floating vegetation.

LEFT, ABOVE The iridescent violet-blue plumage and lurid red bill and legs of the Purple Swamp-hen are unmistakeable.

LEFT, BELOW The diet of the Spanish Terrapin includes all manner of aquatic organisms, including fish, amphibian larvae and insects.

Mammals

Perhaps the most aquatic of Spanish mammals is the Iberian Desman (*Galemys pyrenaicus*, see page 132), while the Water Shrew (*Neomys anomalus*) – a rather large, slate-grey insectivore with a pure-white belly – is also an expert swimmer and diver. Its thick fur traps air bubbles, enabling it to pop to the surface like a cork at the end of a dive.

The extremely hydrodynamic Eurasian Otter (*Lutra lutra*) possesses inter-digital membranes on all four feet that assist it in propulsion, as well as a sleek waterproof coat that dries quickly on leaving the water. Otters can spend almost a minute underwater when hunting down their prey, which consists principally of fish, but also of amphibians, water birds, water voles (*Arvicola* spp.) and invertebrates, especially crayfish. Their dens, which are usually referred to as holts, frequently have an underwater entrance, which helps to protect the young from unwelcome terrestial predators.

ABOVE Eurasian Otters are found throughout peninsular Spain, with the exception of the Mediterranean coastal regions.

BELOW The White-throated Dipper is associated primarily with fast-flowing mountain rivers, often nesting under waterfalls.

WHERE THE LAND MEETS THE SEA

As part of a peninsula jutting out from the rest of Europe, mainland Spain is endowed with almost 5,000 km of coastline, with the Balearic and Canary archipelagos adding a further 3,000 km between them. Rocky shores make up about two-thirds of this total, with a quarter comprising sandy beaches and dune systems, and only about 4 per cent constituting deltas, estuaries and coastal wetlands.

On the whole, rocky shores occur mainly on the Atlantic coasts, both on the mainland and in the Canaries, and are characterized by the continual erosion of sediments, while sandy shores and estuaries are primarily sedimentation zones, and are particularly common along the Mediterranean coast. Nevertheless, both are transitional habitats – halfway houses between terrestrial ecosystems and marine ones – and as such support a flora and fauna with extremely distinctive ecological characteristics.

BELOW Among the few plants able to tolerate constant drenching by sea spray on Mediterranean coastal cliffs is the Yellow Sea Aster.

Many coastal plants possess mechanisms that enable them to cope with the high levels of salinity that are part and parcel of a life by the sea. In essence, these are similar to those displayed by species that inhabit saline soils in Spain's arid lands (see page 50), revolving mainly around the necessity for the concentration of salts in their cell sap to exceed that of sea water to avoid losing water by osmosis. In order to prevent damage to tissues from these high internal salt levels, many plants have fleshy leaves and succulent stems. In addition, some coastal plants – sea-lavenders (*Limonium* spp.), for example – possess specialized glands that enable them to eliminate excess salt as crystals, giving the leaves a whitish tinge.

It has to be said, however, that the vast majority of vascular plants found in coastal ecosystems survive in spite of the salt, not because of it, although it definitely plays a useful role in keeping competitors at bay. By contrast, many of the characteristic animal denizens of Spain's coastal habitats simply cannot live anywhere else, particularly the more pelagic seabirds and the invertebrate inhabitants of rocky shores.

Rocky Shores and Sea Cliffs

Almost all rocky beaches lie at the bases of cliffs that have been cut back progressively by pounding waves. Some of Spain's most impressive sea cliffs are to be found along the north Atlantic shores, in places plunging almost vertically towards the sea for more than 100 m. Given the fact that the tidal range in the virtually enclosed Mediterranean is minimal, the difference between high and low tide rarely exceeding half a metre, and that the prevailing winds come from the northwest, it is not surprising that rocky shores are less common along the eastern seaboard of mainland Spain, although excellent examples of sea cliffs occur around the headland of Cap de Creus, in Catalunya, and on the Balearic Islands, particularly along the north coast of Mallorca, with those at Cap Formentor topping 300 m.

Rocky shores display a distinct zonation of living organisms according to their exposure to the air during the twice-daily tide cycle. The lowest levels, which are uncovered for only short periods before the tide turns and begins to advance up the shore once more, support a community of essentially marine plants, particularly brown seaweeds of the genera *Laminaria* and *Fucus* along Atlantic shores, and *Cystoseira* in the Mediterranean. At higher levels, red and green seaweeds become more abundant, and any animals living here need either to seek refuge in tidal rock pools during low tide, or to have some means of dealing with a prolonged period out of the water. Gastropod molluscs such as periwinkles (*Littorina* spp.), for example, possess a horny operculum that in effect enables them to 'shut the door', thus protecting them from desiccation.

Vascular plants do not put in an appearance until well above the reach of the spring tides, although even here they need to be tolerant of constant sea spray, as well as having to deal with almost continuous pummelling by the wind. Because sea cliffs are by their very nature almost vertical, strong roots are also a must. Plants that have adapted particularly well to these conditions on the shores of the Atlantic include the Sea Spleenwort (*Asplenium marinum*), Rock Sea-spurrey (*Spergularia rupicola*), Rock Samphire (*Crithmum maritimum*) and Thrift (*Armeria maritima*).

The imposing limestone costal cliffs of the Penyal d'Ifac, just north of Benidorm, host an extremely diverse flora, among which are the Sea Mallow (*Lavatera maritima*), locally endemic scabious *Pseudoscabiosa saxatilis* and Yellow Sea Aster (*Asteriscus maritimus*). Here too grow a number of so-called

Dianic endemics – plants that occur only along this stretch of coast and in the Baleares, notably the purplish-pink-flowered campion *Silene hifacensis*. These Dianic species testify to the ancient link between the Sierras Béticas and the archipelago, when the level of the Mediterranean Sea was much lower than it is today.

Typical plants of rocky shores in the Baleares as a whole include *Scabiosa cretica*, the yellow-flowered composite *Launaea cervicornis*, the diminutive pinkish-flowered ragwort *Senecio rodriguezii* and the Tyrrhenian endemic *Bellium bellidioides*. The volcanic coastal cliffs of Cabo de Gata, in eastern Andalucía, host a number of very localized endemic plants, with pride of place going to the pink-flowered snapdragon *Antirrhinum charidemi* and woolly clumps of *Teucrium charidemi*, growing together with the bushy sea-lavender *Limonium insigne*, known only from south-east Spain.

Much more diverse communities occur on the cliff-top plateaux, where more terrestrial plants occur in conjunction

BELOW The volcanic coast of Cabo de Gata, in eastern Andalucía, abuts some of the least polluted waters in the Mediterranean.

with maritime species. Cabo de Peñas, on the Asturian coast, hosts a colourful mosaic of Gorse (*Ulex europaeus* ssp. *maritimus*), St Dabeoc's Heath (*Daboecia cantabrica*), and Cornish, Mackay's and Dorset Heaths (*Erica vagans*, *E. mackaiana* and *E. ciliaris*), none of which is able to attain a height of more than 30 cm or so on account of the fierce winds that constantly sweep across the plateau. In the shelter of these bushes

grow Summer Lady's-tresses (*Spiranthes aestivalis*) and Pale Butterworts (*Pinguicula lusitanica*), with the edges of the cliff being the preferred habitat of the Danish Scurvygrass (*Cochlearia danica*), Sea Carrot (*Daucus carota* ssp. *gummifer*) and the north-west Iberian endemic Portuguese Angelica (*Angelica pachycarpa*).

The myriad small ledges and crevices present on most sea cliffs provide very suitable breeding grounds for seabirds, with craggy offshore islets particularly favoured because of their inaccessibility to predators. The coast of Galicia is a particular hotspot for seabirds in mainland Spain, hosting small breeding colonies of the European Storm-Petrel (*Hydrobates pelagicus*), European Shag (*Phalacrocorax aristotelis aristotelis*) and Lesser Black-backed Gull (*Larus fuscus*), as well as huge numbers of Yellow-legged Gulls (*L. michahellis*). Spain's only breeding populations of Black-legged Kittiwakes (*Rissa tridactyla*) and Common Murres or Guillemots (*Uria aalge*) are also found here, although the latter has declined dramatically in recent years from around 2,000 pairs in 1960 to just a handful today. The Canary Islands also harbour a rich assemblage of nesting seabirds, especially shearwaters and storm-petrels, some of which do not breed elsewhere in Europe.

In the Mediterranean, by contrast, the Balearic cliffs are the only place in the world where you can find breeding Balearic Shearwaters (*Puffinus mauretanicus*). They also harbour good populations of European Storm-Petrels (*Hydrobates pelagicus melitensis*), European Shags (*Phalacrocorax aristotelis desmarestii*), Cory's Shearwaters (*Calonectris diomedea diomedea*), Audouin's Gulls (*Larus audouinii*) and Eleonora's Falcons (*Falco eleonorae*), plus several pairs of Ospreys (*Pandion haliaetus*).

Perhaps the most typical reptiles of rocky coastal areas in the Baleares are Lilford's Lizard (*Podarcis lilfordi*) and the Ibiza Wall Lizard (*P. pityusensis*), both of which are endemic to the archipelago. The most remote cliffs of the Canaries harbour some of the last remaining colonies of the unique Canary Islands giant lizards (*Gallotia* spp., see page 112).

Sedimentary Coasts

Sand Dunes

First and foremost, dunes are dynamic ecosystems continually fed by wind-blown sands from the beach, their advance blocked only by small elevations in the hinterland and by vegetation invading from neighbouring habitats. So-called embryo dunes just behind the high-tide mark represent the least stable habitats, while those furthest from the sea, which are almost completely isolated from the maritime influence, have almost

LEFT, ABOVE The cliff-top plateau of Cabo de Peñas, in Asturias, is the easternmost limit of the Iberian endemic Portuguese Angelica.

LEFT, BELOW The Sea Knotgrass is one of the first species to colonize embryo sand dunes forming beyond the strand-line.

ABOVE Only two breeding nuclei of Black-legged Kittiwakes are present in Spain, both on Galicia's precipitous Costa da Morte.

RIGHT Extinct as a breeding bird in mainland Spain, fewer than 40 pairs of Ospreys remain on the Baleares and Canaries today.

stopped moving and are thus known as fixed dunes. Embryo or primary dunes are constantly exposed to onshore winds, as well as being subject to wave action during the highest tides. Although sand is an exceedingly dry, sterile material, some nutrients and moisture are on hand in the form of decomposing detritus along the strand-line.

These infant dunes are initially colonized by psammophilic grasses such as the Sand Couch (*Elytrigia juncea*) and Lyme-grass (*Leymus arenarius*). Both are perennial species with long roots and lateral and vertical shoots that serve to bind the sands together, creating more stable conditions for the invasion of other plants. Along the Mediterranean coast these might include the Prickly Saltwort (*Salsola kali*), Sea Medick (*Medicago marina*) and the umbellifer *Echinophora spinosa*, with the Sea Knotgrass (*Polygonum maritimum*), Sea Rocket (*Cakile maritima*) and Cottonweed (*Otanthus maritimus*) being more characteristic of Atlantic shores.

White or secondary dunes represent the next stage in the dune succession. These are still rather sparsely vegetated, and

ABOVE The Spiny-footed Lizard's toes are equipped with three rows of tiny keeled scales that help it to get a purchase on unstable substrata.
LEFT Spurge Hawkmoth caterpillars feed voraciously on Sea Spurge, attaining a length of 8–10 cm in just a couple of months.

subject to the constant movement of wind-blown sands inland. The marram-grass *Ammophila arenaria* is the dominant species here, again able to grow both vertically and laterally through the sand, and possessing inrolled leaves that reduce moisture loss through transpiration. Gaps in the marram-grass carpet are colonized by the fluorescent pink-flowered campion *Silene littorea*, Sea Spurge (*Euphorbia paralias*), Southern Birdsfoot-trefoil (*Lotus creticus*), Sea-holly (*Eryngium maritimum*), Sea Bindweed (*Calystegia soldanella*), Coastal Crucianella (*Crucianella maritima*), Sea Daffodil (*Pancratium maritimum*) and a grass known as Hare's-tail (*Lagurus ovatus*).

Moving further inland still, the grey or tertiary dunes get their name from the carpet of lichens, particularly *Cladonia* spp., which covers the sand. Plant diversity is much higher here, with the Atlantic dunes boasting a vibrantly coloured mosaic of the Sand Stock (*Malcolmia littorea*), Jersey Pink (*Dianthus hyssopifolius* ssp. *gallicus*), the white-berried shrub *Corema album*, Spiny Thrift (*Armeria pungens*), fleshy-leaved figwort *Scrophularia frutescens*, the endemic snapdragon *Antirrhinum linkianum*, the everlasting flower *Helichrysum italicum* ssp. *serotinum* and Sea Wormwood (*Artemisia*

campestris ssp. *maritima*), the latter occasionally parasitized by the Sand Broomrape (*Orobanche arenaria*). Sadly, the majority of Spain's tertiary dune systems have vanished under coastal resorts, with Corrubedo in Galicia – its tertiary dunes home to more than 200 species of vascular plant – being the best remaining example on the north Atlantic coast, while the parallel waves of pine-clad dunes in the Doñana National Park take pride of place on Spain's southern shores.

The fauna of Spain's sand-dune habitats includes invertebrates such as the bronze-coloured, highly predatory tiger beetle *Cicindela maritima*, and the Spurge Hawkmoth (*Hyles euphorbiae*), whose extraordinarily robust and colourful caterpillars can be located by examining clumps of their host plant, the Sea Spurge. Spiny-footed Lizards (*Acanthodactylus erythrurus*) and Large Psammodromuses (*Psammodromus algirus*, see page 114) are perhaps the most characteristic reptiles of southern Spanish beaches. The Italian Wall Lizard (*Podarcis sicula*) has been introduced to Menorca and the coasts of Cantabria and Almería, in mainland Spain, where it favours sand-dune systems and rocky shores.

Kentish Plovers (*Charadrias alexandrinus*) are probably the archetypal beach-breeding bird in Spain, the males boasting striking chestnut caps in summer, but they may be accompanied by small colonies of Little Terns (*Sterna albifrons*) along more remote stretches of the Mediterranean and south-west Atlantic shores.

ABOVE Mobile dunes along the coast of the Doñana National Park are heading inland, swallowing the secondary dunes en route.

Shingle Beaches

These stony beaches are relatively rare in Spain, with examples including Mechillueira, on the Atlantic coast of Galicia, and Prat de Cabanes–Torreblanca in València, on the Mediterranean coast. Understandably, shingle beaches are even more hostile habitats for plants than sandy beaches, with a lack of water and nutrients being the main deterrents. On the Atlantic shores, only species such as the Sea Sandwort (*Honckenya peploides*), the eye-catching Yellow Horned-poppy (*Glaucium flavum*), Rock Samphire, Cottonweed and *Scrophularia frutescens* are able to survive. The Valencian enclave is a botanical micro-reserve harbouring a rare assemblage of the joint-pine *Ephedra distachya*, Birthwort (*Aristolochia clematitis*), the Afro-Iberian campion *Silene ramosissima*, the Yellow-horned Poppy, Purple Spurge (*Chamaesyce peplis*), Cottonweed and Golden Samphire (*Inula crithmoides*).

Mudflats and Salt Marshes

The sheltered estuaries that are scattered around the Spanish coastline usually occur at the mouths of rivers. As the flow of fresh water is impeded by its entry to the sea, its capacity to carry the particles of soil that the river has eroded further

ABOVE The huge biomass of invertebrates that lives in mudflats provides food for wintering waders such as Sanderlings (*Calidris alba*).

upstream drops abruptly, resulting in the deposition of large quantities of sediment, forming mudflats. Spain's only signifi-cant delta is the result of the powerful Ebro – Spain's longest river – overcoming the rather listless waters of the Mediterranean, so these water-borne sediments are carried far from the shore before being laid down. Over centuries an enormous, arrow-shaped tract of land has developed, today devoted largely to growing rice, although the seaward margins host sand dunes, coastal marshes and brackish lagoons.

Salt marshes develop where mudflats rise above the level of the lowest tides, showing distinct zones of vegetation according to the length of time different areas are inundated or exposed by the tides, although on the more or less non-tidal Mediterranean shores the vegetation is much more homogenous.

The lowest belt of salt marsh on the Atlantic coast tends to be submerged for all but the lowest spring tides – of which there are two per lunar cycle – and is populated by essentially marine vascular plants such as the Eelgrass (*Zostera marina*) and Dwarf Eelgrass (*Z. noltii*), with flat, ribbon-like leaves. These plants grow along Spain's Atlantic and Mediterranean coasts, but are rarely exposed on the latter, growing at a depth of 1–10 m. Along Mediterranean sandy shores, the eelgrasses give way with depth to undersea meadows of posidonia (see box, opposite) and *Cymodocea nodosa*, which is also found around the coasts of the Canaries. The flowers of all four of these 'sea-grasses' never reach the surface and are pollinated by underwater currents, and the fruits are dispersed by the sea.

Above the eelgrass zone the first true terrestrial plants start to appear – halophytic species that are able to withstand a pro-longed twice-daily submersion in sea water. At the lowest lev-els annual glassworts (*Salicornia* spp.) are dominant, with the Purple Glasswort (*S. ramosissima*) occurring all around the Spanish coast, *S. dolichostachya* confined to the Cantabrian salt marshes, such as the Marismas de Santoña, and *S. emerici* typical of the Ebro Delta. Because they form a dense carpet, almost to the exclusion of all other flowering plants, these suc-culent chenopods trap sediments around their stems, and thus the substratum slowly rises, making way for the next commu-nity in the salt-marsh vegetation succession.

Around the high-tide mark, saltmarsh-grasses (*Puccinellia* spp.) prevail. Creeping stolons up to 50 cm long enable these grasses to spread rapidly, forming a dense, mat-like sward little more than a centimetre tall. Associated species in this belt include the Sea-purslane (*Halimione portulacoides*), some-times parasitized by the yellow spikes of *Cistanche phelypaea* ssp. *phelypaea*), plus the Annual Sea-blite (*Suaeda maritima*), Greater Sea-spurrey (*Spergularia media*), Sea-milkwort (*Glaux maritima*), Sea Plantain (*Plantago maritima*) and Sea Arrowgrass (*Triglochin maritima*). In summer, the marshes turn mauve and yellow as the sea-lavenders (*Limonium* spp.), Sea Aster (*Aster tripolium*) and Golden Samphire come into bloom.

POSIDONIA MEADOWS

The sea-grass *Posidonia oceanica* is basically a terrestrial flowering plant that has returned to the sea. It occurs exclusively in the Mediterranean, where it forms extensive undersea meadows, particularly on sandy substrata, to a depth of about 40 m. It has strap-shaped leaves about 1 cm wide and 30–120 cm long, and thick rhizomes covered with the fibrous remains of the leaves. Balls of these dead plant fibres cover the beaches of the Mediterranean following stormy weather.

Posidonia grows very slowly, and takes centuries to develop into the dense meadows that represent the most mature phase in the sea-floor vegetation succession. In effect, these meadows increase the surface area of the substratum enormously, and support a diverse array of epiphytic marine invertebrates such as hydrozoans, bryozoans and tunicates.

While some species, such as Rock and Violet Sea-urchins (*Paracentrotus lividus* and *Sphaerechinus granularius*), feed directly on the foliage and rhizomes, others hunt down their prey among the leaves, typically starfish of the genera *Asterina* and *Echinaster*, cephalopods, decapods such as *Catapaguroidea timidus* and the Seaweed Shrimp (*Hippolyte inermis*).

A wide range of bony fish is also found here, including the Board-nosed Pipe-fish (*Syngnathus typhle*), White and Saddled Seabreams (*Diplodus sargus* and *Oblada melanura*), Salema (*Sarpa salpa*) and the brightly coloured Long-snouted, Axillary and Ocellated Wrasses (*Symphodus rostratus, Crenilabrus mediterraneus* and *C. ocellatus*).

As it needs sunlight in order to photosynthesize, *Posidonia oceanica* can only grow in very clear waters, and in areas where the coast is particularly affected by building or industry these meadows have all but disappeared. A further threat comes in the form of the non-native leafy green algae *Caulerpa taxifolia* and *C. racemosa*, which are highly competitive species that can oust posidonia within a very short space of time.

BELOW The leaves of the sea-grass *Posidonia oceanica* provide a valuable niche for epiphytic marine invertebrates.

Above this level and out of reach of all but the highest tides, belts of Saltmarsh and Sea Rushes (*Juncus gerardii* and *J. maritimus*) are often accompanied by clumps of Thrift. Brackish pools and ditches in the upper salt marsh host submerged hydrophytes such as Beaked and Spiral Tasselweeds (*Ruppia maritima* and *R. cirrhosa*), Horned Pondweed (*Zannichellia palustris*) and Holly-leaved Naiad (*Najas marina*). Here also grow the Brackish Water-crowfoot (*Ranunculus peltatus* ssp. *baudotii*), Blunt-fruited Water-starwort (*Callitriche obtusangula*) and other species tolerant of brackish waters.

The fine sediments of mudflats and salt marshes are inhabited by all manner of burrowing invertebrates, particularly bivalve molluscs and various species of segmented polychaete worm. These in turn provide food for a wealth of waders, whose long beaks are ideal for delving into the soft sediments, and whose ear openings are positioned further forwards on the head than in other birds, the better to detect vibrations in the mud that might indicate the presence of their invertebrate prey.

Although only a handful of waders nests in Spanish salt marshes – for example Black-winged Stilts (*Himantopus himantopus*), Pied Avocets (*Recurvirostra avosetta*) and Common Redshanks (*Tringa totanus*), principally on the Mediterranean and south-west Atlantic coasts – in the winter and during migration periods these estuarine habitats attract millions of northern European birds in search of a decent meal.

A remarkable degree of specialization in feeding techniques among the various waders ensures that competition is minimal. Short-beaked species such as the ringed plovers (*Charadrias* spp.) feed primarily on organisms that live close to the surface. Those with longer bills can probe more deeply, with Eurasian Curlews (*Numenius arquata*), Whimbrels (*N. phaeopus*) and Black-tailed and Bar-tailed Godwits (*Limosa limosa* and *L. lapponica*) being veritable experts at hooking polychaete worms from their burrows. By contrast, the upturned, flattened bill of the Pied Avocet is used to good effect to scythe through the surface sediments to dislodge prey. Long legs enable their owners to wade into the water to take advantage of subterranean invertebrates that themselves might have emerged to feed.

Some of the largest and best-preserved salt marshes occur in the Ebro Delta, on the Mediterranean coast; the Marsimas del Odiel and the Bahía de Cádiz, on the south-west Atlantic shore; and Umía–O Grove, on the west coast of Galicia. A series of less extensive localities also exists along the Cantabrican coast: Ortigueira, in Galicia; the mouth of the River Eo, on the Galicia–Asturias border; Santoña, in Cantabria; and the Biosphere Reserve of Urdaibai, in the País Vasco.

LEFT, ABOVE Of all the waders that frequent the Spanish coast, the Black-winged Stilt has the longest legs.

LEFT, BELOW Whimbrels occur in Spain only on passage and during the winter, principally along the Atlantic coast and on the Canaries.

ISLAND OUTPOSTS: THE CANARIES

The Canary archipelago comprises seven volcanic islands adrift in the Atlantic Ocean, around 100 km from the coast of north-west Africa and more than 1,100 km from mainland Spain, by which it was annexed in the 15th century. Along with Madeira and the Açores, the Canaries are part of the biogeographic region of Macaronesia, renowned for its incredible plant and animal diversity. The largest island is Tenerife, covering 2,035 sq km and rising 3,715 m above sea level to culminate in Spain's highest peak, El Teide.

Although in the past it has been suggested that the easternmost Canary Islands – Fuerteventura and Lanzarote – were once attached to the African mainland, today most authorities agree that all the islands in the Canary archipelago are truly oceanic, meaning that they have never been linked to a continental land mass at any time. The Canary Islands were in fact formed as a result of eruptive phenomena taking place in zones of weakness in the Earth's crust, more than 2,000 m below the surface of the ocean, and in effect represent the tips of a series of volcanoes, some of which are still active today.

Geological evidence exists to demonstrate that the seven islands of the Canary archipelago appeared at different times. Fuerteventura and Lanzarote, which perch on top of the same block of parent material, are the oldest islands, thought to have reached the surface around 20 million years ago, while the westernmost islands of La Palma and El Hierro are the youngest, considered to be just 1.5–3 million years old. Sporadic volcanic activity has persisted into historic times on all the islands except La Gomera, the smallest of the archipelago, which has been inactive for more than 4 million years. Although the most recent eruption occurred in the south of La Palma, in 1971, the best-preserved volcanic landscape on the archipelago lies in the Timanfaya National Park, on Lanzarote.

Ever since the islands broke free of the ocean they have been subject to the erosive forces of sea, wind and rain. Over

BELOW The remarkable volcanic landscape of the Timanfaya National Park is virtually devoid of vegetation, except for lichens.

ABOVE The Malpaís de La Corona, in northern Lanzarote, backed by the silhouette of the crater of Monte Corona itself.

millennia these sterile mounds of lava and volcanic ash have been weathered to produce small pockets of soil, in which the first plants – arriving as wind- or water-borne seeds – were able to gain a tenuous foothold. Today almost 2,000 species of vascular plant occur on the Canary Islands, more than a quarter of which are found nowhere else in the world.

Similarly, the first animals to colonize the Canaries had to arrive under their own steam, crossing many kilometres of open water to do so. Isolated from continental influences, these species were then at liberty to follow their own evolutionary paths, generating a fauna exceptionally rich in endemic taxa. This is perhaps most evident among the reptiles – 14 unique species are scattered across the archipelago (see page 111) – and the invertebrates, new taxa of which are being discovered every year. The Canaries are also home to six birds (see page 118) and – incredibly – two terrestrial mammals (see page 131) that are found nowhere else in the world.

The principal habitats of the Canary Islands are dictated primarily by climate and altitude. In essence, distinct bands of vegetation have developed at different altitudes, the height at which these occur varying according to whether they are exposed to the north-easterly *alisios* or lie in the rain shadow.

Cardonal–Tabaibal

The basal zone, often called *malpaís* or 'badlands', and much affected by the recent rash of new tourist resorts and banana plantations, encompasses the hottest, driest regions of all the islands. It extends from sea level to around 400 m on north-facing slopes and up to 700 m on south-facing slopes, thus covering the larger part of the eastern isles of Fuerteventura and Lanzarote. The principal vegetation type of this basal zone is referred to as *Cardonal–Tabaibal*, named after the dominant shrubs. In the eastern Canaries great expanses of stony and sandy plains, known locally as *jables*, are also present, and harbour similar plants to those found growing in coastal sands.

Cardón is the local name for *Euphorbia canariensis*, a succulent spurge characterized by great clumps of columnar stems up to 3 m tall, which is surely one of the most memorable plants of all seven islands. In essence, the *Cardón* has adapted to the lack of available water in exactly the same way as the

New World cacti, in a superb example of convergent evolution. The extensive root system absorbs water rapidly when it rains, storing it in the stems for use during drought periods, while the leaves have been reduced to short, curved spines to avoid water loss by transpiration, so photosynthesis is carried out exclusively by the stems. This is obviously such a successful strategy in arid conditions that several other Canary Islands plants have opted for a similar way of life, including the leafless spurge *Euphorbia aphylla*, the very spiny *E. handiensis*, the small, cactus-like *Caralluma burchardii* (family Asclepidaceae) and related species of *Ceropegia*.

The *Tabaibas* also belong to the genus *Euphorbia*, but are leafy shrubs – often known as tree spurges – displaying a much lesser degree of succulence and tending to shed their leaves in times of drought. The most widespread species are *E. balsamifera*, *E. obtusifolia* and *E. regis-jubae*. They often grow in conjunction with *Kleinia neriifolia*, which is morphologically very similar but belongs to the daisy family (Compositae), and the distinctive *Plocama pendula* (family Rubiaceae), which has long, drooping branches.

Typical invertebrates of the *Cardonal–Tabaibal* include the Barbary Spurge Hawkmoth (*Hyles tithymali*), whose caterpil-

ABOVE The Atlantic Lizard is unique to the islands of Fuerteventura, Lanzarote and the Chinojo Archipelago.
LEFT, ABOVE The Teno Peninsula, in north-west Tenerife, harbours one of the best remaining examples of *Cardonal–Tabaibal* in the Canaries.
LEFT, BELOW Like all mantises, *Blepharopsis mendica* is highly predatory, impaling its victims on its spine-tipped front legs.

lars feed on the leaves of the various spurges. By the time they are ready to pupate, these creatures look like fat, black-and-red sausages some 8 cm long. The endemic longhorn beetles *Lepromoris gibba* and *Stenidea albida* both have larvae that develop only within the dead stems of the *Cardón*, while the spectacular, rather spiny mantis *Blepharopsis mendica* – up to 6 cm long and also found in North Africa – lurks among the branches of the tree spurges. Such hot, dry habitats also find favour with a wide range of reptiles, including geckos, skinks and lizards of the genus *Gallotia* (see page 112), as well as with the endemic Canary Shrew (*Crocidura canariensis*).

The most distinguished bird of the basal zone is undeniably the Canary Islands endemic race of the Houbara Bustard (*Chlamydotis undulata fuerteventurae*), the largest bird on the archipelago, standing around 60 cm tall. It occurs exclusively

ABOVE The sandy plains of Fuerteventura and Lanzarote are home to the only European populations of Houbara Bustards.

LEFT Although Cream-coloured Coursers are generally sedentary, it is thought that some of the Lanzarote birds migrate to Africa.

in the extensive arid *jables* of Fuerteventura and Lanzarote, where it is threatened with loss of habitat due to the relentless construction of tourist facilities, and its total population probably does not exceed 600 individuals. Like all bustards, Houbaras are ground-nesting birds, so they are very much at home in these sparsely vegetated habitats, and are also willing to use their long legs to good effect by running away when threatened rather than taking to the air. They are omnivores feeding on seeds, small lizards and invertebrates.

The Cream-coloured Courser (*Cursorius cursor*) is almost impossible to detect if it is not moving, so well does its sand-coloured plumage blend in with its habitat. With a bit of patience, small groups of these birds can be detected sprinting around like miniature roadrunners in the open, arid *jables* of the eastern Canaries. The archipelago represents the principal European breeding locality for this medium-sized wader, harbouring some 2,000 individuals. It is considerably more common on Fuerteventura than Lanzarote and has recently been confirmed as breeding in southern Tenerife.

Other birds characteristic of the basal zone of most of the islands in the archipelago include the Barbary Partridge

(*Alectoris barbara koenigi*), Eurasian Thick-knee (*Burhinus oedicnemus*, represented by two endemic races, *B. o. distinctus* and *B. o. insularum*), the Canary Islands endemic race of the Trumpeter Finch (*Bucanetes githagineus amantum*) and Berthelot's Pipit (*Anthus bertholotii*), the latter with a world distribution confined to the Canary Islands and Madeira. By contrast, the endemic Canary Islands Stonechat (*Saxicola dacotiae*) nowadays breeds only in the more vegetated badlands of Fuerteventura, as does the Canary Islands population of Black-bellied Sandgrouse (*Pterocles orientalis*). The endemic race of the Southern Grey Shrike (*Lanius meridionalis koenigi*) is a conspicuous denizen of the basal zone on Tenerife, Gran Canaria, Fuerteventura and Lanzarote.

Thermophilic Forest

The thermophilic forest is essentially a transitional zone lying above the arid badlands, its upper margin grading into laurel forests on north-facing slopes and pines on the southern flanks of the islands. Ever since the Canaries were first colonized by humans, this has been the most populated zone in the archipelago. It has been much affected by centuries of felling, grazing and agriculture, so that little remains of the climax vegetation today, although enclaves persist on inaccessible sea cliffs and in some of the gorges, such as the Barranco del Infierno, on Tenerife.

ABOVE Canary Palms in the Barranco de la Villa, on La Gomera, in the western Canary Islands.

Because temperatures are slightly lower and rainfall a little higher than they are in the basal zone, stands of endemic Canary Palms (*Phoenix canariensis*) and Canary Junipers (*Juniperus canariensis*) are able to grow here, accompanied by a range of fairly drought-tolerant shrubs such as the olive *Olea europaea* ssp. *cerasiformis*, *Maytenus canariensis* and the deciduous *Pistacia atlantica*. The Canary Palms have long been cultivated, particularly on La Gomera, where a syrup is prepared from the sap and the fronds are used for animal fodder. Together with Date Palms (*Phoenix dactylifera*), they have also been planted extensively for ornamental purposes, but truly wild populations are extremely rare today.

Perhaps the most famous denizen of these warmth-loving forests, however, is the Dragon Tree (*Dracaena draco*), a Macaronesian endemic member of the lily family (Liliaceae). Dragon Trees are much sought after for their dark red sap, colloquially known as 'dragon's blood', which is reputed to have medicinal and magical properties. As a result, only young trees survive in the wild, confined to inaccessible nooks and crannies in a few hot, humid, steep-sided *barrancos* on Tenerife, La

Palma and Gran Canaria. The Dragon Tree is, however, commonly planted in parks and gardens, where it develops into a graceful, umbrella-shaped tree, its single trunk topped by numerous forked branches, at the ends of which grow clusters of sword-shaped leaves.

Laurisilva

As the prevailing northerly winds encounter the abrupt peaks of the westernmost Canary Islands they are forced upwards, so that the air cools and water vapour condenses, creating a dense and persistent cloud layer at between 500 and 1,200 m on the north-facing slopes. This humid montane zone is occupied by the renowned laurel forests – which are locally known as *laurisilva* – of the Canary archipelago.

Wreathed in perpetual mist, the damp, shady woodlands of the *laurisilva* represent some of the last remaining examples of the semi-tropical vegetation that dominated much of the continent of Europe during the Tertiary period, with exceptional stands being preserved within the Garajonay National Park, on the island of La Gomera.

Among the trees of the *laurisilva*, adaptation to high levels of humidity has resulted in an overriding morphological stereotype similar to that frequently encountered in the tropical forests of the world. The trees have tough, evergreen, glossy leaves that have pronounced 'drip-tips'. These ensure that water runs off the leaves easily and does not accumulate to rot the foliage.

As a result of this specialization, it is hard to differentiate between the various tree species that make up the forest canopy, only four of which are in fact laurels (family Lauraceae): *Laurus azorica*, *Ocotea foetens*, *Persea indica* and *Apollonias barbujana*.

The other characteristic trees of the *laurisilva* belong to a wide range of families, including Small-leaved and Large-leaved Hollies (*Ilex canariensis* and *I. perado* ssp. *platyphylla*), in the Aquifoliaceae, *Prunus lusitanica* ssp. *hixa*, in the Rosaceae, the strawberry tree *Arbutus canariensis*, in the Ericaceae, the buckthorn *Rhamnus glandulosa*, in the Rhamnaceae, and *Pleiomeris canariensis* and *Heberdenia excelsa*, in the essentially tropical Myrsinaceae.

In the most ancient of these woodlands, the branches of the trees are interlinked to such an extent that the canopy is continuous. As a result, the forest floor receives virtually no light at all, so that only a few extremely shade-tolerant plants can survive at ground level, for example the orange-flowered foxglove relative *Isoplexis canariensis* and a tall member of the gentian family with large yellow flowers known as *Ixanthus viscosus*.

LEFT, ABOVE Although Dragon Trees are often planted in formal gardens, fewer than 700 individuals are known from the wild on the Canaries.
LEFT, BELOW Wreathed in cloud for much of the year, the laurel forests of Tenerife are festooned with epiphytic mosses and lichens.

Ferns too abound here, notably the spectacular *Woodwardia radicans*, whose 2-metre fronds produce roots where their tips meet the ground, as well as *Dryopteris oligodonta*, *Diplazium caudatum* and the Irish Spleenwort (*Asplenium onopteris*).

Climbing plants such as the blue-flowered bindweed *Convolvulus canariensis*, the exquisite Canary Bellflower (*Canarina canariensis*) and the liliaceous lianes *Smilax canariensis* and *Semele androgyna* scramble through the understorey in order to get closer to the light, while epiphytic lichens, mosses and ferns – particularly *Davallia canariensis* – festoon the trunks of the trees, their water requirements satisfied by the constant mist.

Among the animal inhabitants of the *laurisilva*, the two endemic laurel pigeons undoubtedly take pride of place. Both Bolle's Pigeon (*Columba bollii*) and the Laurel Pigeon (*C. junoniae*) are confined to the islands of La Palma, El Hierro, La Gomera and Tenerife, where they feed almost exclusively on the fleshy fruits of the laurel forest trees. While the Laurel Pigeon tends to nest in crevices or small caves on rocky outcrops, usually just below the *laurisilva* zone in the thermophilic woodlands, Bolle's Pigeon breeds only in the thickest, most mature laurel forests, constructing untidy platforms of sticks in the trees; the clutch size in both species is just a single egg.

Other noteworthy birds of these forests are the Canary Islands Kinglet (*Regulus teneriffae*) and Canary Islands Chiffchaff (*Phylloscopus canariensis*), both of which are also confined to the archipelago.

Canary Pine Forests

Above the sea of cloud that is such a distinctive feature of north-facing slopes, humidity is lower and temperatures decrease markedly, especially at night, despite the fact that the level of insolation is much higher. These fairly harsh conditions give rise to a dry montane zone that extends from about 1,200 m to 2,000 m, while on southerly inclines, in the absence of the laurel forests, it may commence at just 700 m above sea level. The only native tree able to tolerate this marked diurnal temperature variation and

ABOVE The constant semi-tropical climate of the western Canary Islands allows Bolle's Pigeons to breed all year round.

BELOW The exquisite Canary Bellflower is one of the most emblematic climbing plants of the *laurisilva*.

paucity of soil water is the Canary Pine (*Pinus canariensis*), a species unique to the archipelago.

As is the case with the *laurisilva*, Canary Pine forests are absent from the low-lying islands of Fuerteventura and Lanzarote, with the most extensive stands occurring on Tenerife, La Palma, El Hierro and Gran Canaria. The Canary Pine is blessed with an extensive root system that allows it to

ABOVE Only male Blue Chaffinches are actually blue; the females are a dull olive-brown colour.
OPPOSITE At 3,715 m, the volcanic peak of El Teide, on Tenerife, is Spain's highest mountain.

colonize even the poorest of soils, including lava flows and pyroclastic fallout, although under favourable conditions these trees can grow to a staggering 50 m. In addition to this, it is supremely adapted to forest fires, able to shoot from the base even after the tree has been completely destroyed, while the seeds germinate readily after such events.

As pine needles decay extremely slowly, the soil beneath the trees is very poor in nutrients, so that other plants find it difficult to grow here. Among the most characteristic shrubs are the pink-flowered *Cistus symphytifolius* and the legume *Chamaecytisus proliferus*, distinguished by its white flowers, both of which grow only on the Canary Islands.

Not many species of insect find pine needles palatable, but caterpillars of the Canary Islands endemic moth *Macaronesia fortunata* (family Lymantriidae) are the exception to the rule, sometimes reaching plague proportions in the Canary Pine forest. The larvae of the jewel beetle *Buprestis bertholoti* (family Buprestidae) and the bark-gnawing beetle *Temnochila pini* (family Ostomidae) feed on the wood of dead pine trees.

Two endemic races of the Great Spotted Woodpecker (*Dendrocopos major*) – *D. m. thanneri* on Gran Canaria and *D. m. canariensis* on Tenerife – have their strongholds in the Canary Pine forests, where night-flying insects provide food for the Canary Big-eared Bat (*Plecotus teneriffae*), which is also confined to the archipelago. The best-known denizen of this habitat, however, is the Canary endemic Blue Chaffinch (*Fringilla teydea*), the males of which are stunning slate-blue birds, rather stockier than the common or garden Chaffinch (*F. coelebs*). They are often seen in small groups in the more open pine woodlands of Tenerife's Corona Forestal Natural Park, for-

aging for the pine kernels that make up a large part of their diet.

The High Mountain Zone:
Retamar–Codesar

Above an altitude of 2,000 m, night-time environmental conditions are so harsh that trees cannot grow. Here the Canary Pines are replaced by a unique high-mountain scrub that is known locally as *Retamar–Codesar*, once again named for its dominant species. Only La Palma and Tenerife reach this altitude in the Canaries, peaking respectively at Roque de los Muchachos (2,426 m) and El Teide (3,715 m), which rises head and shoulders above the rest of the archipelago.

The principal shrubs of these bleak, 'cold-desert' habitats are the legumes known as the *Retama del Teide* (*Spartocytisus supranubius*) and *Codeso de Cumbre* (*Adenocarpus viscosus*), both of which are unique to the archipelago. Although the *Retama del Teide* is quite a large bush, many of the other shrubs of these heights adopt the classic cushion habit that is so typical of high-mountain species, in winter resembling nothing so much as a flock of 'vegetable sheep'. Among the most commonplace species are the crucifers *Descurainia bourgaeuana* and *Erysimum scoparium*, with yellow and pink flowers respectively, the figwort *Scrophularia glabrata*, the scabious-like *Pterocephalus lasiospermus* and the composites *Argyranthemum teneriffae* and *Cheirolophus teydis*.

Perhaps the most memorable plant of these heights, however, is the spectacular viper's-bugloss known as *Taginaste Rojo* (*Echium wildpretii*), which is common in Tenerife's Cañadas del Teide National Park, but extremely rare on La Palma. In late summer, each large, silvery leaf-rosette produces a fat spike several metres tall, studded with hundreds – if not thousands – of small, blood-red flowers. Less imposing is the delightful little Teide Violet (*Viola cheiranthifolia*), which holds the record for being the highest naturally occurring plant of the archipelago, growing among loose screes to a height of some 3,500 m near the summit of Tenerife. The closely related *V. palmensis* occupies a similar niche amid the peaks of La Palma's Caldera de Taburiente National Park.

The only birds that breed habitually in the high mountain zone are Kestrels (*Falco tinnunculus canariensis*), Barbary Partridges, Rock Doves (*Columba livia canariensis*), Plain Swifts (*Apus unicolor*) and Berthelot's Pipits.

Possibly of greater interest are the unusually large numbers of endemic invertebrates that can be found only here, notable among which are the Canary Blue (*Cyclirius webbianus*) butterfly, whose caterpillars feed on leguminous shrubs in all vegetation zones of the islands, the grasshopper *Sphingonotus willemsei*, the longhorn beetle *Hesperophanes roridus* and the

ABOVE The vast crater that surrounds the peak of El Teide is littered with pyroclastic 'shrapnel'.

diminutive flightless mantis *Pseudoyersinia teydeana*, which can sometimes be seen sunning itself on the flowers of *Pterocephalus lasiospermus*. The Tenerife Lizard (*Gallotia galloti*) is also very common in the high mountain habitats of both La Palma and Tenerife.

Coastal Habitats and Offshore Islets

The shores of the western islands of the archipelago are for the most part rocky and precipitous, whereas on the eastern islands low-lying sandy beaches abound, with sea cliffs present only in western Fuerteventura and northern Lanzarote. The most remote stretches of cliffs are noted for their populations of giant Canary lizards and frequently possess a rich endemic flora. For example, the Riscos de Famara, located in northwestern Lanzarote, are home to a unique assemblage comprising the sea-lavender *Limonium bourgaeui*, the pink-flowered, shrubby bindweed *Convolvulus lopez-socasi*, the fleshy-leaved tree-plantain *Plantago famarae* and the yellow-flowered composite *Reichardia famarae*, as well as succulent rosettes of *Aichryson tortuosum* and *Aeonium balsamiferum*.

Given their oceanic location, it is perhaps not surprising that the coastal cliffs of the Canary Islands – particularly those of undisturbed offshore islets such as Tenerife's Roques de Anaga and the Archipiélago Chinojo, off northern Lanzarote –

harbour important seabird assemblages, including populations of a number of species that do not breed elsewhere in Spain. Birds such as the Little Shearwater (*Puffinus assimilis baroli*), Bulwer's Petrel (*P. bulwerii*), Band-rumped or Madeiran Storm-Petrel (*Oceanodroma castro*) and White-faced Storm-Petrel (*Pelagodroma marina*) are pelagic species that spend most of their lives at sea. The White-faced Storm-Petrel – which was only discovered as a breeding bird on the Canary Islands in 1987 – is the rarest of these species, with a tiny colony of less than 30 pairs known only from the offshore islets of northern Lanzarote.

More widespread seabirds that breed in the archipelago include Cory's Shearwaters (*Calonectris diomedea borealis*) and European Storm-Petrels (*Hydrobates pelagicus*). Manx Shearwaters (*Puffinus puffinus*), however, more commonly nest in colonies in well-vegetated inland gorges, often excavating burrows between the roots of the trees.

In addition, three species of raptor typically breed on the Canary Islands coastal cliffs, all of which have suffered enormously from habitat loss and disturbance in recent times. The Osprey (*Pandion haliaetus*) is almost extinct as a breeding bird in the Canaries today, with fewer than 20 pairs remaining, principally on Lanzarote, La Gomera and El Hierro, although it was once widespread on all the islands. Eleonora's Falcons (*Falco eleonorae*) nest only on the islets to the north of Lanzarote today, while Barbary Falcons (*F. pelegrinoides*) are nowhere common, but probably breed on all seven of the main islands.

Important coastal sand-dune systems occur at Maspalomas on Gran Canaria and Corralejo on Fuerteventura, with less extensive communities of this type occurring on all the principal islands.

These habitats are populated by an interesting shrubby flora dominated by the fleshy chenopod *Traganum moquinii*, the succulent *Zygophyllum fontanesii*, distinguished by its almost grape-like leaves, the white-leaved birdsfoot-trefoil *Lotus sessilifolius*, the sea-lavender *Limonium pectinatum* and the widespread yellow-flowered composites *Schizogyne sericea* and *Launaea arborescens*. On Fuerteventura and Lanzarote, open sands are populated by the charming little *Androcymbium psammophilum*, which is a rare winter-flowering member of the lily family.

The most characteristic bird to breed in undisturbed sandy coastal habitats is the Snowy or Kentish Plover (*Charadrius alexandrinus*). Although Common Terns (*Sterna hirundo*) once nested in large colonies on the eastern islands, today the population probably does not exceed 50 pairs, confined mainly to remote coastal habitats on the islands of La Gomera, La Palma and El Hierro. Even more tragically, the distinctive all-black Canary Islands Oystercatcher (*Haematopus meadewaldoi*) – equipped with startlingly red legs and bill – which formerly bred on rocky coasts and sandy shores on the eastern Canary Islands, has not been seen since 1981 and is almost certainly extinct. In winter, large numbers of migratory waders flock to the sandy shores to roost and feed, including many common European species.

ABOVE The setting sun catches the sheer Famara cliffs, with Lanzarote's most extensive sand-dune system in the foreground.
BELOW Like the Peregrine, of which it is sometimes considered a subspecies, the Barbary Falcon feeds mainly on pigeons.

Chapter 2
THE WILDLIFE OF SPAIN

Lying at a biological crossroads between Europe and Africa, the Spanish flora and fauna has affinities with both. Nevertheless, because Spain is more or less isolated from Europe by the 400-km chain of the Pyrenees, and from Africa by the Straits of Gibraltar, a high degree of endemism is in evidence, particularly among relatively sedentary groups such as plants, amphibians, reptiles and mammals. This trend is even more pronounced on the remote oceanic Canary Islands, where plants and animals have been evolving in isolation for at least 1.5 million years. The enormous range of habitats found in Spain has given rise to an impressive array of species, the diversity of which is unrivalled in Western Europe. There are more than 8,500 plant taxa, about 47,000 insects, including two-thirds of all European butterflies and moths, and some 30 amphibians, 60 reptiles and 90 mammals. About 337 bird species rear their young in Spanish territory, while the proximity of Spain to Africa is responsible for the existence of a major migration route – the Western Mediterranean Flyway. This is used biannually by millions of birds travelling between their northern European breeding localities and wintering grounds in sub-Saharan Africa.

LEFT Even though Spanish Brown Bears (*Ursus arctos*) are among the smallest members of their species in the world, they can still weigh up to 250 kg.

FLORA

The vascular flora (ferns and flowering plants) of Spain, including the Balearic and Canary Islands, has been estimated to number about 8,500 species and subspecies – more than in any other European country with the exception of Turkey. Around 1,500 of these taxa are unique to mainland Spain and the Baleares, while due to its oceanic origin the Canary archipelago is a particular hotspot of biodiversity, with the level of endemism among the native flora approaching 40 per cent.

The remarkable diversity of the Spanish flora can be attributed to a number of factors. Perhaps most significantly, the Iberian Peninsula lies at a crossroads between two distinct climatic regimes – Atlantic and Mediterranean – with a semi-tropical element present in the Canary Islands. In addition, a wide range of rock types is present in Spain, ranging from the volcanic elements of the Canaries to base-rich limestones and siliceous granites and gneisses on the mainland and in the Baleares, while the degree of altitudinal variation is simply enormous, ranging from sea level to more than 3,700 m.

BELOW, LEFT An annual member of the caper family, *Cleome violacea* is found principally in western and southern Iberia.
BELOW, CENTRE The delicate white flowers of the Three-leaved Snowflake bloom in early spring on sandy soils in southern Spain.
BELOW, RIGHT With a Spanish range limited to Andalucía, *Biscutella frutescens* is a chasmophyte of vertical limestone crags.

Further botanical diversity is almost certainly derived from the fact that Spain has at various times in the distant past been linked by land bridges to both North Africa and islands in the western Mediterranean. As a result, about 500 of Spain's vascular plant species are considered to be Afro-Iberian endemics: that is, they occur only in Spain, Portugal and north-west Africa. Examples of these plants are particularly abundant in southern Spain. They include such emblematic species as the Spanish Fir (*Abies pinsapo*), the birthwort *Aristolochia baetica*, the bizarre *Cleome violacea*, the frothy-flowered crucifer *Biscutella frutescens*, the peony *Paeonia coriacea*, the diminutive yellow-flowered violet *Viola demetria*, the sun-rose *Halimium ocymoides*, the tall-spiked viper's-bugloss *Echium boissieri* and Three-leaved Snowflake (*Leucojum trichophyllum*) in the daffodil family (Amaryllidaceae). Similarly, the so-called Tyrrhenian element of the Spanish flora – plants that are found on the Balearic Islands and also occur on Corsica,

Sardinia and Sicily – includes species such as the daisy-like *Bellium bellidioides*, the creeping toadflax *Cymbalaria aequitriloba*, Autumn Arum (*Arum pictum*) and Dragon's Mouth (*Helicodiceros muscivorus*).

Origins of the Spanish Flora

Throughout the early part of the Tertiary period (65–25 million years ago), the climate over much of Europe was much hotter and more humid than it is today, partly because the continent itself was located at more southerly latitudes. At this time, the vegetation of Iberia was dominated by tropical and subtropical elements, but during the Miocene epoch (25–5 million years ago) the climate started to cool, allowing coniferous and deciduous trees to gain a tenuous foothold in the northern part of the peninsula. By the middle of the Pliocene epoch (about 3 million years ago), a marked reduction in summer rainfall was responsible for the development of large areas of sclerophyllous vegetation similar to that which characterizes the Mediterranean region today.

A radical change in environmental conditions affected Iberia in the Quaternary period (2 million years ago to the present), with the Pleistocene glaciations favouring more cold-tolerant Euro-Siberian forests and banishing the Mediterranean and subtropical vegetation to the very warmest coastal enclaves of the peninsula, although this process was reversed to some extent in the interglacial periods. In the Canary Islands at this time, however, the combination of a more southerly location and the moderating effect of the ocean maintained healthy expanses of semi-tropical vegetation – the *laurisilva* (see page 82) – which has persisted in the western islands to the present day.

Small enclaves of the Tertiary semi-tropical vegetation can also still be found in the hottest, wettest parts of mainland Spain, such as the sheltered gorges of Las Villuercas in Extremadura, Los Alcornocales in Andalucía and the Boquerón del Estena in the Cabañeros National Park. Typical Tertiary relict species of these semi-tropical forests include the Portugal Laurel (*Prunus lusitanica*), *Rhododendron ponticum* ssp. *baeticum* and myriad ferns – *Woodwardia radicans*, *Christella dentata*, *Asplenium hemionitis* and *Davallia canariensis*, to name but a few.

Around 10,000 years ago, when the ice sheets finally retreated northwards for the last time, the current vegetation pattern was laid down, although by Neolithic times around 5,000 years ago, humans were also starting to make their mark. Euro-Siberian vegetation dominated the northernmost reaches, with deciduous woodlands and semi-natural grass-lands in the Atlantic realm of northern and western Spain, grading into extensive coniferous forests in the Pyrenees. Across much of the rest of Spain and the whole of the Balearic archipelago, the climax vegetation at that time was Mediterranean forests of evergreen oaks and pines, but during

BELOW The least accessible slopes of the Monfragüe National Park still harbour remnants of the primeval Mediterranean forest.

the long period of human occupation much of the primeval woodland was replaced by *dehesas*, groves of Wild Olive (*Olea europaea*) and Carob (*Ceratonia siliqua*), vineyards, arable land, pastures and secondary scrub communities.

Glacial Relics

Only in the highest mountains of Spain did the most cryophilic species manage to survive the withdrawal of the ice sheets, where they were effectively cut off from neighbouring populations. In the intervening period, many localized endemic taxa have evolved from these ancestral Arctic plants, so that some of the richest botanical assemblages in Spain today occur in the alpine zone (see page 22). Among the Iberian endemic species that are thought to have evolved from the Mountain Thrift (*Armeria alpina*), for example, are *A. cantabrica* in the mountains of the north of the peninsula, *A. bubanii* and *A. muelleri* in the Pyrenees, *A. bigerrensis*, which is represented by three unique subspecies in the central Spanish ranges, *A. godayana* in the Sierra de Gúdar, in Teruel, and *A. splendens*, which is found at altitudes of up to 3,200 m in the Sierra Nevada, in Andalucia.

Spain's highest peaks also harbour a number of so-called Arctic–Alpine plants – species whose present-day distributions extend well to the north of the Arctic Circle, but which are also found in mountain ranges in more temperate regions of the northern hemisphere. Among the most noteworthy examples are the Alpine Clubmoss (*Diphasiastrum alpinum*), Glacier Crowfoot (*Ranunculus glacialis*), Starwort Mouse-ear (*Cerastium cerastoides*), Dwarf Willow (*Salix herbacea*), Trailing Azalea (*Loiseleuria procumbens*), Blue Heath (*Phyllodoce caerulea*), Purple Saxifrage (*Saxifraga oppositifolia*), Mountain Avens (*Dryas octopetala*), Sibbaldia (*Sibbaldia procumbens*) and Snow Gentian (*Gentiana nivalis*).

Saxifrages

Of the 120-odd European species of saxifrage, more than half occur in Spain and 19 are found nowhere else in the world. *Saxifraga nevadensis*, as its name suggests, grows only in the Sierra Nevada, while the eye-catching yellow-flowered *S. felineri* is confined to the Picos de Europa, in northern Spain. Similarly, *S. moncayensis* is unique to El Moncayo – the highest peak in the Sistema Ibérico, at 2,313 m – while *S. vayredana* and *S. genesiana* grow only in the granitic Montseny massif in Catalunya. Among a whole host of species that are unique to the Pyrenees are the delightful Water Saxifrage (*S. aquatica*), Yellow Saxifrage (*S. aretioides*) and Reddish Saxifrage (*S. media*).

Perhaps the most spectacular species in the genus is the Pyrenean Saxifrage (*S. longifolia*), which – despite its vernacular name – has a world distribution that includes not only the Pyrenees, but also several ranges in eastern Spain and the Atlas Mountains in Morocco. The leaf-rosettes take up to six years to

mature and may grow to about 14 cm in diameter, at which point they produce fabulous flowering spikes up to 60 cm long and 15 cm wide, each of which may contain 400–800 individual white blooms. While the plant is in flower the leaves begin to wither, and by the time the seed has ripened the plant is dead and the six-year cycle must start all over again.

Many saxifrages that grow on calcareous rocks, such as Pyrenean and Reddish Saxifrages, Blue Saxifrage (*S. caesia*) and Livelong Saxifrage (*S. paniculata*), are able to extract lime from the substratum through their roots and then secrete it as droplets of calcium carbonate in solution. This then dries to a whitish crystalline substance, encrusting the leaves and possibly helping to protect the plants from excessive levels of ultra-violet radiation.

Endemic and Threatened Plants

About 1,500 species of vascular plant in mainland Spain and on the Balearic Islands are found nowhere else in the world, with the genera *Dianthus* (pinks, family Caryophyllaceae), *Limonium* (sea-lavenders, Plumbaginaceae), *Teucrium*, *Sideritis* and *Thymus* (Labiatae), *Linaria* (toadflaxes, Scrophulariaceae), *Centaurea* (knapweeds, Compositae) and *Narcissus* (daffodils, Amaryllidaceae, see box, page 95) being particularly rich in endemic taxa.

This figure would be even higher were it to include plants whose distribution does not extend further north than the high Pyrenees, albeit on the French side of the chain. Such a level of endemism is considerably higher than that of any other Western European country. Continental France, for example, has fewer than 100 endemic taxa, while mainland Portugal harbours about 150 unique species.

Of the 1,500 or so vascular plant recorded in the Baleares, about 8 per cent are unique to the archipelago. The island of Mallorca is particularly rich in endemic species, around 30 of them confined to the Serra de Tramuntana. Among the rarer endemics are the buttercup *Ranunculus weyleri*, *Paeonia cambessedesii*, Mallorcan violet (*Viola jaubertiana*), the crucifer *Naufraga balearica* (a monospecific genus), *Vicia bifoliolata*, *Daphne rodriguezii* and *Centaurea balearica*. In fact, almost 30 per cent of the European plant taxa listed in the Annexes of the European Habitats Directive occur in mainland Spain and the Balearic archipelago, for the most part because they are endemic species with a very localized distribution.

OPPOSITE, CLOCKWISE FROM THE TOP, LEFT The glacial relic Mountain Avens grows almost at sea level north of the Arctic Circle, and at 2,800 m in the Pyrenees; *Saxifraga felineri* is known only from vertical limestone crags above 2,000 m in the Picos de Europa, northern Spain; like many endemic plants – from various families – found in the Balearic Islands, the peony *Paeonia cambessedesii* possesses purple-backed leaves; the Spanish name for the spectacular Pyrenean Saxifrage is *Corona de Rey*, literally, 'king's crown'.

The situation on the Canary Islands is even more remarkable, with almost 600 endemic taxa recorded, particularly within the genera *Aeonium* (family Crassulaceae), *Echium* (Boraginaceae), *Micromeria* and *Sideritis* (Labiatae), and *Sonchus* and *Argyranthemum* (Compositae), each of which contains more than 20 species unique to the archipelago. Even more extraordinary is the fact that the islands harbour no less than 19 endemic genera, for example *Parolinia* (Cruciferae), *Greenovia* (Crassulaceae) and *Tinguarra* (Umbelliferae).

Because they grow on remote islands, these endemic plants have nowhere else to go if things get rough, so the badly considered placement of a single tourist resort can wipe out a whole species. Of the 1,414 variously threatened plants that make up the *Red List of Spanish Vascular Flora*, published in 2000, 458 occur only on the Canary Islands within Spanish territory. Compare this to the 845 taxa cited for the whole of the Spanish mainland and it is clear that the Canary Islands

flora has its back against the wall. It has been estimated that almost 70 per cent of the Canary Islands endemic flora is in danger of extinction.

Some of the most severely threatened plants of the archipelago, with less than a dozen individuals surviving in the wild, are the rock-roses *Helianthemum aganae* on La Gomera and *H. inaguae* on Gran Canaria; three distinctive birdsfoot-trefoils, *Lotus eremiticus* and *L. pyranthus* on La Palma and *L. maculatus* on Tenerife; and the labiate *Sideritis amagroi*, again on Gran Canaria. Sadly, the Tenerife endemic shrub *Kunkeliella psilotoclada* (family Santalaceae) has not been seen since 1983 and is probably extinct, a victim of uncontrolled livestock grazing on the island. *Normania nava* (family Solanaceae), which formerly grew in the laurel forests of Anaga, again on Tenerife, followed suit in 1984.

Spanish Orchids

Considered by most botanists to be the most 'advanced' of all vascular plants, the family Orchidaceae is a relatively young group in evolutionary terms, and is thought to have arisen some 50–60 million years ago. Because the family is still evolving, hybridization is rife and there is widespread discrepancy as to the exact number of taxa, but recent estimates put the global total at about 850 genera comprising some 20,000–30,000 species. The majority of orchids occur in tropical regions, but approximately 250 species are present in Europe.

According to the fairly broad-brush classification proposed in volume XXI of *Flora Iberica* (2005), in which numerous taxa suggested in alternative treatments are not recognized, peninsular Spain and the Balearic Islands are home to 24 orchid genera represented by 87 species. The Canary Islands harbour just eight species of orchid, three of which – the Three-lobed Habenaria (*Habenaria tridactylites*), Canary Islands Orchid (*Orchis canariensis*) and Metlesic's Orchid (*Barlia metlesicsiana*) – are unique to the archipelago.

Orchid flowers are usually borne in racemose inflorescences. Each bloom has six perianth segments arranged in an inner and outer whorl, with the uppermost segment of the inner whorl differing in shape, size and colour from the others. This segment is called the lip, and in some species it may be extended backwards to form a spur that is often much longer than the flower itself and may contain nectar. When in bud the lip is located at the top, but in most species, as the flower opens it twists through 180 degrees – a process known as resupination – so that the lip effectively becomes the lowest segment, providing a platform for polli-

BELOW Canary endemic sow-thistles of the genus *Sonchus* tend to be shrubs or perennial herbs up to 3 m tall.

NARCISSI

The genus *Narcissus*, whose members are commonly referred to as daffodils or narcissi, is commonly believed to have originated in Spain, from whence various species have radiated out across Europe, extending into North Africa and as far east as the Balkan Peninsula. Although the taxonomy of the genus is constantly undergoing revision, recent studies suggest that Spain, as befits the epicentre of the genus, is home to almost 50 native species – roughly three-quarters of the world total – many of which are unique to the country.

The majority of daffodils produce large, showy flowers, most of which are scented and are thus probably insect pollinated. They are popular garden plants, and many hybrids and cultivars have been developed for the horticultural market. Among the more showy wild species are *Narcissus pseudonarcissus* and the Pheasant's-eye Narcissus (*N. poeticus*). Although most narcissi flower in the spring, several species characteristic of Mediterranean habitats bloom in the autumn, including the diminutive Tapeinanthus (*N. humilis*), whose flowers face skywards, and the aptly named Autumn Narcissus (*N. serotinus*). Some species are even in flower right through the winter, including the Polyanthus Narcissus (*N. tazetta*) and Paper-white Daffodil (*N. papyraceus*).

The smallest of the Spanish daffodils are only a few centimetres tall, as exemplified by *N. hedraeanthus* from the mountains of south-eastern Spain, *N. asturiensis* from the Cordillera Cantábrica and the Hoop-petticoat Daffodil (*N. bulbocodium*). By contrast, the magnificent flowering stems of *N. longispathus*, which is endemic to wet flushes in the mountains of Jaén (Andalucía), sometimes reach a height of 175 cm. Much sought after by collectors in the past, this species is endangered in the wild today and is therefore protected by Andalucían and European law. In fact, of the 12 narcissi listed in the European Habitats Directive as being in need of strict protection, 11 occur in Spain, while no less than 17 species are so endangered that they are included in the *Red List of Spanish Vascular Flora*.

Although most members of the genus produce flowers in various shades of yellow, the delightful White Hoop-petticoat Daffodil (*N. cantabricus*) and the multi-flowered *N. dubius* and Paper-white Daffodil have all-white blooms, while the slender *N. viridiflorus*, which grows only in the province of Cádiz (Andalucía), has striking green flowers; because these are strongly scented and open mainly at night, it is thought that they are probably pollinated by moths.

BELOW Subalpine pastures in the Cordillera Cantábrica are studded with the diminutive blooms of *Narcissus asturiensis* in early spring.

BELOW *Narcissus dubius* flowers from December to May in the limestone mountains behind Spain's eastern Mediterranean coast.

nating insects to land on. It is particularly broad in species such as the Pink Butterfly Orchid (*Orchis papilionacea*) and Heart-flowered Serapias (*Serapias cordigera*), and extremely long in the aptly named Lizard Orchid (*Himantoglossum hircinum*).

Although in tropical regions many orchids are epiphytic, all the European species are terrestrial. In most cases, their roots are 'infected' with mycorrhizal fungi, which assist the plant in absorbing dissolved nutrients from the soil. In green-leaved taxa, these symbiotic fungi serve merely to supplement the plant's diet, but in saprophytic species (see page 34), in which

chlorophyll is absent, they play a crucial role in enabling the plant to obtain nutrients for growth and reproduction.

Among the more localized species of orchid in the Iberian Peninsula are Spanish endemics such as the recently described helleborine *Epipactis cardina*, unique to eastern Spain, and *Orchis cazorlensis*, which is confined to Mallorca and the mountains in the south and east of the country. The diminutive, deep-red vanilla orchid *Nigritella gabasiana* is known only from the Cordillera Cantábrica and the Pyrenees, including the French side of the chain, while the distinctive, pale-green-flowered

ABOVE Some of the most handsome populations of Pink Butterfly Orchids can be found in the hay meadows of northern Spain.

ABOVE The dark cavity formed by the 'hood' of the Heart-flowered Serapias tempts bees to spend the night, thus effecting pollination.

tongue orchid *Serapias perez-chiscanoi* is unique to western Iberia. Afro-Iberian endemic orchids include *Epipactis lusitanica* and *Serapias strictiflora*.

Perhaps the most intriguing European orchids are those belonging to the genus *Ophrys*. Their most distinctive feature is that the lip of the flower bears more than a passing resemblance to a female insect, particularly bees and wasps of the order Hymenoptera, in morphology, colour and hairiness. In addition, the scent exuded by the flower imitates the female pheromones of a particular species of hymenopteran, thus attracting the male insect, which then tries to copulate with the flower. This process, known as pseudocopulation, results in the sticky pollinia of the orchid becoming attached to the insect, and subsequently being deposited when it tries to mate with another flower: cross-pollination is thus accomplished.

To the human eye, among the most convincing Spanish examples are the Fly Orchid (*O. insectifera*), pollinated by wasps of the genus *Argogorytes*, and the Mirror Ophrys (*O. speculum*), whose flowers apparently only attract reddish male *Dasyscolia ciliata* wasps. The success or otherwise of this process depends on the plant catching the attention of male insects that have not yet learned to distinguish the orchid flower from the real McCoy. For this reason, many *Ophrys* orchids flower very early, and can be seen in bloom from March onwards in the Mediterranean *garrigue*. Common species on limestone bedrock are Dull, Bumble-bee, Yellow, Woodcock and Early Spider Ophrys (*Ophrys fusca, O. bombyliflora, O. lutea, O. scolopax* and *O. sphegodes*), while the Sawfly Ophrys (*O. tenthredinifera*) is typical of siliceous soils.

The genus *Ophrys* is extremely variable, and although many authors recognize a seemingly infinite number of taxa, volume XXI of *Flora Iberica* distinguishes just 12 true species. The handsome Atlas Ophrys (*O atlantica*) is an Afro-Iberian endemic, while the Aveyron Orchid (*O. aveyronensis*) is known only from northern Spain and southern France. Two subspecies – Bertoloni's Ophrys (*O. bertolonii* ssp. *balearica*) and the Iberian Ophrys (*O. speculum* ssp. *lusitanica*) – are considered to be unique to the Iberian Peninsula and Baleares.

INVERTEBRATES

Spain harbours a veritable treasure trove of 'creepy crawlies'. Exact figures are hard to come by, but a recent estimate puts the number of insects alone at about 47,000, with dozens of new species being discovered every year. On the Canary Islands, almost 7,000 species of terrestrial arthropod have been catalogued to date, of which roughly 40 per cent are unique to the archipelago.

The monumental diversity of invertebrates found in Spain is for the most part the domain of professional scientists, so only the best-known groups are dealt with here.

Dragonflies and Damselflies

The Spanish quota of dragonflies and damselflies (order Odonata) currently stands at 79 species, 3 of which occur only on the Canary Islands: the endangered Island Darter (*Sympetrum nigrifemur*), a Macaronesian endemic, plus the Violet Dropwing (*Trithemis arteriosa*) and Sahara Bluetail (*Ischnura saharensis*), both of which are also found in North Africa, but not in Europe. Although no odonates are unique to Spain, the sand-coloured Faded Pincertail (*Onychogomphus costae*) and the delicate Iberian Bluetail (*Ischnura graellsii*) have a world range restricted to Iberia and north-west Africa.

Broadly speaking, damselflies (suborder Zygoptera) are slender creatures that tend to fold their wings together when at rest, and are thus distinguished from the more robust dragonflies (suborder Anisoptera), which generally perch with outstretched wings. In all cases they are highly predatory insects both as adults and in the larval stage. The larvae are always aquatic, shedding their skins several times during their development to allow growth to take place. For the final moult, when they turn into winged adults, the larvae abandon the water, usually by climbing up the stems of emergent plants, leaving behind perfectly formed larval skins called exuviae. Most Spanish odonates spend the winter as eggs or larvae, but the adults of the Common Winter Damselfly (*Sympecma fusca*) emerge in late summer and overwinter as adults, with reproduction talking place the following spring.

As might be expected, natural wetland habitats harbour the best odonate assemblages, with different species associated with flowing and standing water. For example, the white-legged damselflies or featherlegs (*Platycnemis* spp.), and clubtails (*Gomphus* spp.), are particularly linked with streams and rivers, while still waters are favoured by chasers (*Libellula* spp.).

RIGHT, TOP The Common Clubtail (*Gomphus vulgatissimus*) occurs in just a handful of sites in Spain, and is thus classified as Vulnerable.
RIGHT, BOTTOM Spanish populations of the Beautiful Demoiselle (*Calopteryx virgo*) belong to the subspecies *meridionalis*.

ABOVE The bright colours of the Iberian endemic Spanish Tiger serve to warn potential predators that it is poisonous.

ABOVE Spanish Puss Moths are found throughout Spain and Portugal and the Balearic Islands, the adults flying between April and July.

Wetlands are among the most threatened of all the world's habitats, subject to drainage, pollution and – in the case of rivers – artificial reinforcement of the margins, which destroys emergent vegetation, with odonate populations often suffering in the process. Today some of the rarest European species are the Mercury Bluet (*Coenagrion mercuriale*), Pronged Clubtail (*Gomphus graslinii*), Splendid Cruiser (*Macromia splendens*) and Orange-spotted Emerald (*Oxygastra curtisii*).

The Pronged Clubtail, whose world distribution is confined to south-western France and Iberia, has only been recorded in Spain since the 1970s, particularly in the western reaches, with just 8–10 nuclei known today. Its habitat requirements in Spain appear to be very specific: slow-flowing rivers on a soft substratum, with shady margins fringed with emergent vegetation and a sunny centre. The Splendid Cruiser, thought to be a relic

BELOW Like all burnet moths, *Zygaena fausta* is a day-flying species, frequenting dry, calcareous hillsides up to 1,500 m.

of the warmer climate that prevailed in Tertiary times, has a rather similar world distribution to the Pronged Clubtail, but appears to be a much rarer and more localized beast, with the best-known Spanish populations occurring in Galicia. Its larvae are known to bury themselves in muddy substrata close to the edges of rivers, often beneath overhanging bushes. The Orange-spotted Emerald is another Tertiary relic, also found in Italy and north-west Africa. It is more abundant and widespread in Spain than the previous two species, known from Galicia, Asturias, Álava, Extremadura, Andalucía and Catalunya.

Moths and Butterflies

It has been estimated that about 7,000 species of Lepidoptera occur in Europe, of which roughly 2,600 are so-called 'macro-moths' and about 400 are butterflies, the rest being 'micro-moths'. Peninsular Spain and the Balearic Islands harbour 230 species of butterfly as well as more than 1,600 macro-moths – about 60 per cent of the European total in each case.

Spanish Endemic Moths

Among the most noteworthy Spanish moths are those that are unique to the Iberian Peninsula and the northern flanks of the Pyrenees just across the French border. They include five members of the family Arctiidae (tiger moths and allies): the extremely handsome Spanish Tiger (*Hyphoraia dejeani*), Iberian Footman (*Eilema predotae*), Spanish Footman (*Coscinia romeii*), Latreille's Pellicle (*Artimelia latreillei*) and Spanish Pellicle (*Ocnogyna zoraida*). Other Spanish endemics are the Spanish Puss Moth (*Cerura iberica*), in the family Notodontidae (prominent and kitten moths), and Southern and Lajonquière Lappets (*Psilogaster loti* and *Phyllodesma kermesifolia*) in the Lasiocampidae (eggar moths), as well as approximately 40 members of the Geometridae. More than 700 noctuids (family

Noctuidae) occur in Spain, among them numerous endemics, some of which are confined to just one small area, for example *Euxoa nevadensis* in the Sierra Nevada, *Agrotis sabulosa* in the coastal sand dunes of Huelva and *Discestra gredosi* in the Sierra de Gredos.

Burnet Moths

Of the 70 species of burnet moth (genus *Zygaena*) in the world, 22 occur in the Iberian Peninsula and Baleares. They are extremely colourful, day-flying species whose forewings are patterned predominantly with spots or bands of red and/or yellow on a blackish background, often sporting a deep metallic green or bluish sheen when newly emerged. Such bright colouration serves to warn potential predators that burnet moths are unpalatable – even toxic – creatures, releasing poisons such as hydrogen cyanide if attacked.

Although all the forewing patterns are based on six spots, in some species these have merged to form distinctive bands of colour, as in the Transparent Burnet (*Z. purpuralis*), *Z. contaminei*, Royal Burnet (*Z. sarpedon*), *Z. osterodensis*, *Z. nevadensis* and *Z. romeo*. In some of the spotted species, the red blotches are ringed with haloes of white, cream or pale orange – *Z. carniolica*, *Z. occitanica*, *Z. fausta* and *Z. hilaris*, for example – while in others the red markings are distinctively edged with black or dark blue, as for example in *Z. rhadamanthus* and the White-collared Burnet (*Z. lavandulae*).

For the most part, burnet moths are on the wing in the summer months, flying only on warm, sunny days and particularly favouring flowers with pink or mauve blooms – scabiouses, thistles and knapweeds – from which they extract nectar with their long probosces. Because their wings are relatively narrow and their bodies fairly stout, burnet moths are unable to fly long distances, so a large number of distinct races have evolved in discrete geographical areas.

Only one species of burnet moth is endemic to Spain: *Z. ignifera*, whose forewings are a vivid reddish-orange and bear only vestigial black markings. This species is confined to a series of small, isolated populations in eastern Spain, where the adults fly from June to August at altitudes of 900–1,800 m, particularly favouring dry, open habitats. The larvae feed on species of horseshoe vetches (*Hippocrepis* spp.).

Hawkmoths

Of the 33 European hawkmoths (family Sphingidae), 22 are known to occur regularly in Spain. All are eye-catching, robust moths, with long, narrow wings that are capable of rapid, powerful flight,

ABOVE The streamlined body and long, pointed wings of the Small Elephant Hawkmoth are designed for fast, manoeuvrable flight.

favouring long-distance migrations in some species. Most hawkmoths have a well-developed proboscis, sometimes several times as long as the body, enabling them to collect nectar from flowers while in flight. Many have vernacular names indicating the favoured larval food plants, and in most cases the caterpillar bears a distinctive 'horn' at the end of the abdomen.

BELOW Broad-bordered Bee Hawkmoths have extremely long proboscies, enabling them to feed from tubular flowers without landing.

When at rest during the day, hawkmoth hindwings are not visible, and the forewings are cryptically coloured in order to help the moths remain undetected by predators, with the green-marbled wings of the Lime Hawkmoth (*Mimas tiliae*), for example, perfectly camouflaged against sun-dappled foliage, In several species, however, the hindwings are brightly coloured, and if displayed rapidly they may serve to scare off potential predators. The hindwings of the Eyed Hawkmoth (*Smerinthus ocellatus*) sport well-marked ocelli that resemble the eyes of a much larger beast, while vivid yellow flashes are present on the hindwings of Death's Head and Willowherb Hawkmoths (*Acherontia atropos* and *Proserpinus proserpina*). Similarly, Striped and Privet Hawkmoths (*Hyles livornica* and *Sphinx ligustri*), possess vivid pink or red colouration on the hindwings and body.

Many hawkmoths have a pan-European distribution and are found across most of peninsular Spain, including the Privet Hawkmoth, Spurge Hawkmoth (*Hyles euphorbiae*) and day-flying Hummingbird Hawkmoth (*Macroglossum stellatarum*), while the Small Elephant Hawkmoth (*Deilephila porcellus*) occurs only in the northern half of the Iberian Peninsula. By contrast, the Greater Spurge Hawkmoth (*Hyles nicaea*) is more or less confined to the Mediterranean coasts of Europe, including southern and eastern Iberia, while the Southern Pine Hawkmoth (*Hyloicus maurorum*) is known only from south-western France, Iberia and north-west Africa.

More localized species in Spain, with rather disjunct distributions, include the rare Willowherb Hawkmoth and the day-flying Broad-bordered and Narrow-bordered Bee Hawkmoths

BELOW With wings almost a hand-span across, the nocturnal Great Peacock Moth is Europe's largest lepidopteran.

(*Hemaris fuciformis* and *H. tityus*), so named for their transparent wings. The Balearic Islands are home to just eight hawkmoths, but among these is the Smoky Spurge Hawkmoth (*Hyles dahlii*), which is known only from Corsica, Sardinia and the Baleares, although individuals have been known to reach the Catalan coast on migration. Similarly, Andalucía sees regular incursions of the Greater Silver-striped Hawkmoth (*Hippotion osiris*), an essentially African species that is not known to occur anywhere else in Europe. Among the half-dozen hawkmoths found on the Canary Islands is the Barbary Spurge Hawkmoth (*Hyles tithymali*), a widespread African moth that has also been cited on Crete and Malta.

Emperor Moths

Of the seven native European species of emperor moth (family Saturniidae), five are present in Spain: the Spanish Moon Moth (*Graellsia isabelae*), Tau Emperor (*Aglia tau*), Little Peacock (*Saturnia pavoniella*), Emperor Moth (*S. pavonia*) and the magnificent Great Peacock Moth (*S. pyri*), the largest of all European moths, with a wingspan of up to 15 cm. In all adult emperor moths the proboscis is vestigial and non-functional, so that they are unable to feed. They therefore depend solely on stored food reserves while they find a mate and lay their eggs, and for this reason the caterpillars are extremely corpulent. Male emperor moths have strongly feathered antennae, the better to detect pheromones emitted by the females.

The Spanish Moon Moth is an unmistakable creature, with pale bluish-green wings boldly veined with reddish-brown, each of which is punctuated by a central 'eye'. The characteristic long tails of the hindwings are best developed in the male, but the female is slightly larger in size, with a wingspan of up to 10 cm. Although not very rare, the Spanish Moon Moth occurs only in pinewoods in Spain and the western Alps.

Spanish Moon Moths are found in four main nuclei in Spain: the Pyrenees, the Sierra de Guadarrama, the southern Sistema Ibérico, centred on the Serranía de Cuenca, and the more southerly sierras of Alcaraz (Albacete) and Cazorla and Segura (Andalucía). The eggs are laid in the spring or early summer, and the larvae feed voraciously on the needles of Scots or Black Pines (*Pinus sylvestris* or *P. nigra* ssp. *salzmannii*) for about two months, reaching about 8 cm in length by the time they are ready to pupate. At this point the caterpillars construct silken cocoons at ground level, in which they spend the winter. The adult moths emerge between mid-March and mid-June of the following

ABOVE The ocelli of the Spanish Heath serve to divert the point of attack of a predatory bird or lizard away from the head and body.

ABOVE Chapman's Ringlet is the largest member of the genus *Erebia*, found only in León, Asturias, Cantabria and Palencia.

year, depending on latitude and altitude (150–1,800 m), flying at dusk and during the night.

Spanish Endemic Butterflies

Of the butterflies known to occur in mainland Spain and the Baleares, 16 are found nowhere else in the world: 11 blues (family Lycaenidae) and 5 members of the Satyridae (browns). Five of the endemic blues belong to the taxonomically difficult genus *Agrodiaetus*. Forster's Furry Blue (*A. ainsae*) is known only from the limestone plateaux of northern Spain; Oberthür's Anomalous Blue (*A. fabressei*) is unique to similar habitats in northern and eastern Spain; Agenjo's Anomalous Blue (*A. agenjoi*) and the Catalan Furry Blue (*A. fulgens*) occur only in north-eastern Spain; and the Andalusian Anomalous Blue (*A. violetae*) flies only in the mountains of eastern Andalucía and Albacete.

Other Spanish endemic lycaenids include Carswell's Little Blue (*Cupido carswelli*), which is restricted to the mountains of south-eastern Spain, and the Azure Chalkhill Blue (*Lysandra caelestissima*), which is confined to the Montes Universales in eastern Teruel. In addition, two species are known only from the Sierra Nevada: Zullich's Blue (*Agriades zullichi*) and the extremely rare Nevada Blue (*Plebicula golgus*).

More widespread Iberian endemic lycaenids are the Panoptes Blue (*Pseudophilotes panoptes*) and Mother-of-Pearl Blue (*Plebicula nivescens*), while the Spanish Argus (*Aricia morronensis*) is present in a number of widely scattered colonies across Spain, as well as just extending into France on the northern flank of the Pyrenees, where it is very local.

Among the Spanish endemic members of the Satyridae are Zapater's Ringlet (*Erebia zapateri*), restricted to limestone habitats in the southern Sistema Ibérico; Chapman's Ringlet (*E. palarica*), the largest species in the genus, which flies in flowery meadows amid *Genista* scrub in the western and central

Cordillera Cantábrica; and the Spanish Brassy Ringlet (*E. hispania*), confined to the Sierra Nevada. The remaining two endemic satyrids have only recently been upgraded to species in their own right: the Andalusian False Grayling (*Arethusana boabdil*), confined to south-eastern Spain, was formerly considered to be a subspecies of the False Grayling (*A. arethusa*), while the Spanish Heath (*Coenonympha iphioides*), previously a subspecies of the Chestnut Heath (*C. glycerion*), occurs only in damp places in the northern half of the Iberian peninsula.

In addition, there exists a whole suite of species known only from Spain in Europe, although they are also found in Africa or the Middle East. These include Zeller's Skipper (*Borbo borbonica*), the Spanish Chalkhill Blue (*Lysandra albicans*) and

BELOW The eastern Spanish endemic Zapater's Ringlet is on the wing between late July and early September.

CANARY ISLAND LEPIDOPTERA

The Canary Islands are home to over 500 species of Lepidoptera, more than a quarter of which are found nowhere else in the world. Four butterflies are endemic to the western islands of the archipelago. They are the endangered Canary Islands' Large White (*Pieris cheiranthi*), found on Tenerife and La Palma, the Canary Blue (*Cyclirius webbianus*), a widespread species found from the lowlands up to altitudes of 3,500 m in the Cañadas del Teide National Park, the Canary Grayling (*Pseudotergumia wyssii*) and the Canary Speckled Wood (*Pararge xiphioides*). In addition, the Canary Red Admiral (*Vanessa vulcanica*), a denizen of the laurel forests, completes its life cycle only on the Canaries and Madeira, although as a vagrant it may reach Western Europe, while the African Migrant (*Catopsilia florella*), which first became established on the Canaries in 1965 and had spread to all islands by 1995, is not known to breed elsewhere in Europe.

Notable Canary Island endemic moths include the Chaperon (*Canararctia rufescens*, family Arctiidae), the day-flying clearwing *Bembecia vulcanica* (family Sesiidae), the pine-forest pest *Macaronesia fortunata* (family Lymantriidae) and the endangered noctuid *Agrotis fortunata*, whose world distribution is confined to the badlands of El Médano, Tenerife, where it is threatened by uncontrolled tourist development.

ABOVE The closest known relative of the Canary Blue is *Cyclirius mandersi*, endemic to Mauritius and thought to be extinct.

the cryptically coloured Southern Hermit (*Chazara prieuri*), as well as butterflies typical of semi-desert conditions such as the Desert Orange Tip (*Colotis evagore*), Greenish Black-tip (*Euchloe charlonia*) and diminutive Common Tiger Blue (*Tarucus theophrastus*), whose larvae feed only on the spiny shrub *Ziziphus lotus*.

The Genus *Maculinea*

The so-called 'large blues' of the genus *Maculinea* are represented by five species in Europe, four of which occur in Spain. These rare butterflies have a complicated life cycle in which the caterpillars first feed on plant material but later parasitize the nests of various species of ant. In the case of the Dusky Large Blue (*M. nausithous*), for example, the eggs are laid only on the flowerheads of the Great Burnet (*Sanguisorba officinalis*), which in Spain grows solely in damp meadows in the north. When they hatch the caterpillars feed on the flowers and fruits, falling to the ground after the third moult – usually by the beginning of September – where they wait to be collected by ants, either *Myrmica rubra* or *M. scabrinodis*. Once safely ensconced inside the anthill, the Dusky Large Blue caterpillars spend the winter feeding on the ant larvae, tolerated only because they secrete a substance that imitates the scent of the ant grubs. The following summer the caterpillars pupate in the interior of the anthill, emerging as adults in July.

The Dusky Large Blue is the most endangered member of the genus *Maculinea* in Spain, known from only about a dozen widely dispersed localities in the Cordillera Cantábrica, northern Soria and the Sierra de Guadarrama, with each colony often containing less than 100 individuals. Any change in land use could wipe out a colony in a few years, with the major threat to the Cordillera Cantábrica nuclei being the abandonment of the traditional extensive cattle-rearing regime and the consequent invasion of scrub into the meadows.

The other species of *Maculinea* exhibit very similar life cycles, although the larval food plants and ant species vary. The caterpillars of the Mountain Alcon Blue (*M. rebeli*), for example, feed almost exclusively on the developing fruits of the Cross Gentian (*Gentiana cruciata*) and are collected by ants of the species *Myrmica schencki*. Those of the Alcon Blue (*Maculinea alcon*) favour Marsh Gentian (*Gentiana pneumonanthe*) flowers and are able to parasitize nests of several species of *Myrmica*. Although over most of Europe Large Blue (*Maculinea arion*) caterpillars feed on various species of thyme, in Spain they prefer the Wild Marjoram (*Origanum vulgare*), with the host ants being either *Myrmica sabuleti* or *M. scabrinodis*. None of these three species is quite as rare in Spain as the Dusky Large Blue, with the Alcon Blue being found in widely dispersed colonies across northern Iberia, the Mountain Alcon Blue occurring only in the Pyrenees and the province of Teruel, and the more commonplace Large Blue having a distribution that takes in the Pyrenees, northern Spain and the Sistema Ibérico. Because their specialized life cycles are so vulnerable to disruption, however, all four *Maculinea* species are listed on numerous Red Lists, both national and international.

Spiders

The class Arachnida in peninsular Spain and the Baleares contains 13 orders, among them true spiders (Araneae or Aranei), scorpions (Scorpiones) and three orders of harvest-spider (super-order Opiliones). On the Canary Islands, approximately 800 species of arachnid have been described to date, almost half of which are endemic to the archipelago.

The order Araneae is an immensely diverse group, with mainland Spain and the Baleares harbouring more than 50 families containing almost 1,200 species. Among those that might catch your eye are the ladybird spiders of the genus *Eresus* (family Eresidae), of which there are four species in mainland Spain and one, *E. crassitibialis*, on the Canary Islands. The vernacular name refers to the spectacular blood-red abdomen of the males, which in *E. cinnaberinus* is distinctively marked with four large black spots arranged in a square. Ladybird spiders inhabit silk-lined tubes in the ground, from which the all-black, velvety females rarely emerge. Only males and spiderlings are likely to be encountered wandering outside these burrows.

The crab spiders (family Thomisidae) are distinguished by their distinctive sideways gait and extremely elongated first two pairs of legs, an adaptation that helps them to grab their prey. They often secrete themselves in flowers, from which they ambush unwary nectaring insects. In some species the abdomen is distinctly triangular in shape, as for example in *Thomisus onustus*, in which the female may be white, yellow or pink, able to slowly change colour to match its surroundings. The more globose females of *Misumena vatia* adopt a similar strategy, and can be pale green, white or yellow, often bearing thin reddish lateral stripes, while the much smaller males have a whitish abdomen bearing two longitudinal black stripes. Another very distinctive species of crab spider is *Synaema globosum*, with a striking yellowish-orange, black-patterned abdomen, while *Misumenops tricuspidatus* and *Heriaeus hirtus* are greenish species that lie in wait amid leafy vegetation.

Spiders from many different families are responsible for the typical, more or less circular webs that can be seen among bushes all over Spain. Those of the genus *Argiope* (family Araneidae) are fairly easily recognized, as they possess an additional reinforcement known as a stabilimentum: a thicker zigzag ribbon of silk positioned vertically on either side of the centre. Three species of *Argiope* occur in Spain, the most distinctive of which is undoubtedly *A. lobata*, in which the black

ABOVE The most widespread species of the genus *Maculinea* is the Large Blue, with a distribution extending from Europe to Japan.

and white, somewhat flattened females possess 3–4 broad lateral lobes on either side of the abdomen. Much more common, however, is *A. bruennichi*, in which the striking females, each usually seen sitting in the centre of her web, have a large, egg-shaped abdomen sporting horizontal black and yellow stripes. The males are minute by comparison and are frequently eaten by the females, often while mating is in progress.

The only species of arachnid protected by the European Habitats Directive is *Macrothele calpeiana*, a funnel-web spider (family Hexathelidae) that typically constructs its web in pre-existing holes and crevices in warm, damp Cork Oak woodland in Andalucía (and possibly North Africa). With a body that is up to 35 mm long, *M. calpeiana* is one of Europe's largest spiders, with an aggressive reputation and a painful bite to match. Luckily it is a predominantly nocturnal species, in this way avoiding daytime predators as well as the risk of desiccation.

BELOW Female *Argiope bruennichi* spiders usually construct their webs in long grass close to the ground.

AMPHIBIANS

Spanish amphibians can be neatly divided into two groups: the tailed amphibians (order Caudata), which include salamanders and newts, and the tailless amphibians (order Anura), covering six families of frogs and toads. Of the 30 naturally occurring species of amphibian in Spain, 11 are endemic to the Iberian Peninsula.

All amphibians have relatively smooth, moist skins, and most adopt an aquatic existence during the breeding season in order to complete their life cycles. As they are much at risk from desiccation during very dry weather, they are almost always confined to humid habitats and are often active only at night. Amphibian eggs are usually coated with a gelatinous layer and in most cases are laid in water, where they hatch into aquatic larvae called tadpoles. After a period spent feeding and growing, which may last for several seasons under particularly severe conditions, the tadpoles metamorphose into recognizable miniature versions of their parents, although they may not reach maturity for a number of years.

Because amphibians have an innate intolerance to sea water they are unable to colonize oceanic islands, and as a result there are no native species on the Canaries. As the Balearic archipelago was once linked to mainland Spain, however, it is home to the endemic Mallorcan Midwife Toad (*Alytes muletensis*), as well as the only Spanish population of the Green Toad (*Bufo viridis*), although this was probably introduced in the Bronze Age. The North African Fire Salamander (*Salamandra algira*) and the painted frog *Discoglossus scovazzi* reach Spanish territory only in Ceuta and Melilla.

Salamanders and Newts

All eleven species of salamander and newt that occur in Spain belong to the family Salamandridae. Some are principally terrestrial for most of their lives, such as Golden-striped and Fire Salamanders (*Chioglossa lusitanica* and *Salamandra salamandra*), but the majority pursue a more aquatic lifestyle and are rarely found far from water.

The yellow and black Fire Salamander is one of the most variable of all the Spanish amphibians, with a number of distinct races having been described from different parts of the country. Thus, animals from the Pyrenees and Cordillera Cantábrica (*S. s. fastuosa* and *S. s. bernardezi*) may boast broad yellow stripes rather than the typical spots, while those in the high Gredos (*S. s. almanzoris*) are virtually black, and some of the more southerly populations (*S. s. morenica*) contain individuals liberally blotched with red. Fire Salamanders secrete an irritant substance from glands on their backs when threatened, and their vivid colouration has probably evolved to remind would-be predators that they taste bad.

The Fire Salamander is also curious among European amphibians in that instead of laying eggs the females give birth

BELOW The eye-catching striped, rather than spotted, Fire Salamanders from Asturias belong to the subspecies *bernardezi*.

BELOW Male European Brook Newts have shorter, higher tails than the females, and generally do not exceed 14 cm from nose to tail.

to 10–70 larvae. In the case of some of the high-mountain races, the brood consists of a much smaller number of fully metamorphosed salamanders, 3–5 cm in length, which are thought to cannibalize the other larvae inside their mother.

Although some of the Spanish species, such as Fire Salamanders, and Palmate and Alpine Newts (*Lissotriton helveticus* and *Mesotriton alpestris*), are widespread across Europe, others are confined to the Iberian Peninsula, with by far the most localized distribution displayed by the Montseny Brook Newt (*Calotriton arnoldi*). This species, which was first described in 2005, occupies an area of just 40 sq km in the Montseny massif, north-east of Barcelona, and has a world population estimated at fewer than 1,500 individuals. It is superficially similar to the European Brook Newt (*C. asper*) of the Pyrenees, but has a much less tubercular skin and lacks the pale dorsal stripe of the latter.

Both of these brook newts spend their lives in fast-flowing mountain streams, requiring very cold, well-oxygenated waters, and as a result are threatened by activities such as the felling of trees nearby, which often increases the turbidity and temperature of the water.

The Sharp-ribbed Newt (*Pleurodeles waltl*) is the largest tailed amphibian in Spain, attaining a maximum length of about 30 cm including the tail. It occurs mainly in Mediterranean habitats to altitudes of about 1,500 m, and has a world distribution that includes Portugal and northern Morocco. When threatened, the spiny rib tips that give this species its name protrude through the skin, and as these are associated with a series of prominent poison glands, any predator intending to make a meal of a Sharp-ribbed Newt might well think twice.

The rather oceanic climate of western Iberia is much favoured by several somewhat localized members of the Salamandridae, the most noteworthy of which is the Golden-striped Salamander. This short-legged, extremely svelte species has an almost cylindrical body and a very long tail, and is endemic to north-western Spain and the northern half of Portugal. It is predominantly nocturnal or crepuscular, and lives near unpolluted watercourses in Atlantic forests, where it feeds on small arthropods after trapping them with its sticky, protractile tongue.

Another Iberian endemic is the Southern Marbled Newt (*Triturus pygmaeus*), this time with a marked south-westerly distribution. It is only in recent years that this diminutive creature – rarely more than 12cm in length including the tail – has been separated taxonomically from the rather larger Marbled Newt (*T. marmoratus*) that occurs in much of Spain, Portugal and western France.

Both these species of newt are characteristically bright green mottled with black, with the females generally sporting a vivid orange line down the centre of the back, and the males a pronounced dorsal crest during the breeding season. The even smaller Bosca's Newt (*Lissotriton boscai*), which rarely attains 10 cm in total length, is also confined to the western half of Iberia.

One curious phenomenon that is displayed by some species of tailed amphibian is that of neoteny (which is also known as paedomorphism). Neotenous individuals are larvae that fail to metamorphose but grow to adult size, sometimes even becoming sexually mature. This condition is sometimes observed in high-altitude populations of Sharp-ribbed and Alpine Newts.

BELOW Sharp-ribbed Newts hunt largely by scent, feeding on aquatic invertebrates, small fish and amphibians.

BELOW Male Marbled Newts sport a well-developed dorsal crest during the breeding season.

CLOCKWISE, FROM THE TOP, LEFT Male Common Midwife Toads take responsibility for the fertilized eggs until they are ready to hatch; West Iberian Painted Frogs typically inhabit dense herbaceous vegetation, but are rarely found far from water; adult Parsley Frogs are tiny creatures, the females rarely more than 5 cm long, and the males even smaller – their bodies are studded with elongated warts in undulating longitudinal rows; during the breeding season, the usually nocturnal Western Spadefoot may be active during the day.

Frogs and Toads

Unlike newts and salamanders, adult frogs and toads are tailless, possessing short, rather squat bodies and long hind legs. Although a common perception is that frogs generally have smooth, moist skins, while toads are dry and warty, in fact there is no taxonomic distinction between the two types, with species boasting both vernacular names often occurring within the same family.

In the newts and salamanders fertilization is internal: after an elaborate courtship display, the male produces a mass of sperm known as a spermatophore, which the female then collects in her cloaca. When frogs and toads mate, however, the male grasps the female tightly while the eggs are being laid –

a state known as amplexus – then squirts sperm over the eggs to fertilize them externally.

Midwife Toads and Painted Frogs

These amphibians belong to the family Discoglossidae and are distinguished morphologically by the fact that they have non-protractile, disc-shaped tongues, while most other frogs and toads have long, sticky tongues that can be flipped out to trap prey. Unlike most anurans, midwife toads mate on land, during which the female produces a small number of rather large eggs linked together in a 'rosary'. Following fertilization, the male winds this egg-string around his hind legs and proceeds to carry it about with him for about a month until the eggs are ready to hatch, at which point he kicks it off into a suitable water body. Each male may simultaneously carry the egg-strings of several females.

Midwife toads are typically somewhat plump creatures with warty skins, large heads and prominent eyes with vertical pupils. Both males and female sing during courtship, producing a rather distinctive call not dissimilar to the electronic 'beeps' produced by supermarket checkouts. The Common Midwife Toad (*Alytes obstetricans*) is found across most of the northern half of Spain, as well as in Western Europe and North

Africa, while the Iberian Midwife Toad (*A. cisternasii*) is unique to central and south-western parts of the Iberian peninsula. In 1995, a third Spanish mainland species – the Southern Midwife Toad (*A. dickhilleni*) – was brought to light. It is thought to be confined to mountainous regions in the south-east of the country, at altitudes of up to 2,100 m.

Perhaps the most interesting member of the group, how-ever, is the Mallorcan Midwife Toad (*A. muletensis*), first described from fossil remains in 1977 then discovered as a liv-ing creature three years later. This Balearic toad almost cer-tainly evolved from an ancestral mainland species that was stranded some 2 million years ago when the level of the Mediterranean Sea rose for the last time. It is the smallest, slimmest member of the genus, with the adults rarely exceed-ing 4 cm in length, and is endemic to the island of Mallorca, where it was once widely distributed. Due to loss of wetland habitat and predation by the introduced Viperine Snake (*Natrix maura*), however, today the Mallorcan Midwife Toad is con-fined to precipitous limestone gorges in the Serra de Tramuntana, with a population of a few thousand individuals restricted to an area not greater than 200 sq km.

The Iberian Peninsula is also home to two endemic species of painted frog. The West Iberian Painted Frog (*Discoglossus galganoi*), as its name suggests, occurs in the western reaches of the peninsula, principally on siliceous soils. The rather smaller East Iberian Painted Frog (*D. jeanneae*) is confined to Andalucía and central and eastern parts of Spain, particularly favouring lime-rich bedrock. Both are rather stocky creatures up to 8 cm in length, with heart-shaped pupils and variously blotched or striped skins.

Spadefoots and Parsley Frogs

The only Spanish member of the family Pelobatidae is the Western Spadefoot (*Pelobates cultripes*), which is also found in Portugal and France. The relatively short-limbed adults can attain lengths of 11 cm, and are distinguished by their heavily ossified heads, vertical pupils and a prominent 'spade' on the inner edge of each hind foot. These flattened appendages are employed for burrowing in loose or sandy soils. During very dry periods the Western Spadefoot will dig itself an almost ver-tical burrow, up to a metre deep, in which to await the return of more favourable conditions. The tadpoles are extremely large, often more than 10 cm long, although the adults rarely exceed 3 cm in length.

Spain harbours two of the three species of parsley frog (fam-ily Pelodytidae) in the world, so named for their green-speckled skins. Although related to spadefoots, they are much smaller and slimmer, with longer legs that lack the hind-foot appendages. The Parsley Frog (*Pelodytes punctatus*) occurs in northern and eastern Spain, as well as in France and northern Italy, while the Iberian Parsley Frog (*P. ibericus*), which was only recognized as a distinct species in 2000, has a markedly southern Iberian distribution, with 90 per cent of the world

ABOVE Stripeless Tree Frogs are usually bright green, although bluish individuals are known from near Barcelona.

population occurring in Andalucía. Unlike most species of amphibian, tadpoles of this genus can tolerate fairly saline waters, with those of the Iberian Parsley Frog often recorded from the margins of continental endorheic lagoons and in coastal marshes, although they have also been cited at alti-tudes of up to 2,000 m in the Sierra Nevada.

Tree Frogs

For many people, tree frogs (family Hylidae) are tropical forest creatures, so it is perhaps somewhat unexpected to find two species in Spain. Both are plump little frogs, vivid lime-green in colour, with long legs and digits tipped with disc-shaped adhesive pads. Tree frogs are the only European amphibians to climb to any great extent, and they are rarely encountered at ground level except during the breeding season. The Common Tree Frog (*Hyla arborea*) is a widespread European species inhabiting much of Spain except the extreme east and south. It bears lateral stripes that extend from the eye almost to the tips of the hind legs, whereas in the Stripeless Tree Frog (*H. merid-ionalis*), the stripes do not extend much beyond the head. This

ABOVE For much of the year, Common Toads can be found in fairly dry habitats, hiding away by day and emerging at dusk to hunt.

latter species has a rather peculiar distribution in Spain, occurring in the south-western quadrant and again in Catalunya, whence it continues into France and Italy, recorded from just a few scattered localities in between. It is also present in northwest Africa.

Typical Toads and Frogs

The 'typical' toads of the family Bufonidae – with horizontal pupils and characteristically large paratoid glands at the back of the neck – are represented by two native species in Spain. Both the Common Toad (*Bufo bufo*) and Natterjack Toad (*B.*

BELOW Pyrenean Frogs are the smallest members of the family Ranidae in Europe, reaching a maximum length of just 5 cm.

calamita) are widespread in Spain and other parts of Europe, occupying habitats from sea level to around 2,500 m. The Common Toad is undoubtedly one of Spain's largest autochthonous amphibians – there are records of females over 20 cm in length – yet the recently metamorphosed adults are tiny, infrequently exceeding 15 mm, and many succumb to desiccation and predators. To offset these losses, each female lays a phenomenal number of eggs. The characteristic 'ticker-tape' egg-strings – produced two at a time – can be several metres long and may contain more than 8,000 eggs. A similar reproductive strategy is employed by the less robust Natterjack Toad, which often sports a yellowish dorsal stripe and is renowned for its habit of 'running' over short distances, rather than crawling or hopping.

Members of the family Ranidae, or 'typical' frogs, are characterized by their horizontal pupils, streamlined bodies and the presence of two distinct, raised lines down their backs, known as dorsolateral folds. Their relatively long legs are used with great effect to leap on land and swim powerfully when in the water. Five native species and a number of hybrids have been cited in Spain, the most widespread of which is the Iberian Water Frog (*Rana perezi*), found throughout the peninsula except in the very high mountains, and also in southern France. The croaking chorus of this frog is surely one of the most evocative sounds of a Spanish wetland, particularly as it is one of the few Spanish amphibians to be active during the day.

Common Frogs (*R. temporaria*), elsewhere so abundant in Europe, are restricted to the northernmost reaches of Spain, where they may reach altitudes of 2,700 m. The Agile Frog (*R. dalmatina*) is another widespread European species, although in Spain it is confined to a small area of humid deciduous forest at 500–600 m above sea level in Euskadi and Navarra. The Iberian Frog (*R. iberica*), which is endemic to the north and west of the peninsula, is a slimline species distinguished by its long hind legs, widely separated, parallel dorsolateral folds and a pale central stripe on the throat. Its counterpart in the Pyrenees is the homonymous Pyrenean Frog (*R. pyrenaica*), whose world distribution is limited to the central and western parts of these mountains. Pyrenean Frogs are often fairly uniform in colour, ranging from cream or cinnamon to olive-grey, and are more aquatic than many members of this family, spending much of their lives in mountain streams with fast-flowing, cold, well-oxygenated waters: a habitat they may share with the European Brook Newt.

REPTILES

More than 60 terrestrial species of reptile are native to peninsular Spain, the Canary Islands and the Baleares, with a further 15 or so essentially North African species cited from the Islas Chafarinas, the Isla de Alborán and the Spanish enclaves of Ceuta and Melilla, on the coast of Morocco.

The major taxonomic division within the Spanish reptiles separates the tortoises, terrapins and sea turtles (order Testudines), all of which possess a protective bony shell, from the order Squamata, which includes a diverse array of geckoes, skinks, legless and lacertid lizards and snakes.

Most Spanish terrestrial reptiles possess a single row of conical or cylindrical teeth in each jaw and are clad in a skin made up of numerous horny scales, which can be shed periodically to allow for growth. Like amphibians, reptiles are poikilothermic – that is, they depend on external heat sources, principally the sun, to raise their body temperatures to a level at which they can become active. As a result, most species of reptile are diurnal and many become inactive in cold weather, with high-mountain species hibernating for most of the year.

Fertilization is internal, and while most Spanish reptiles lay eggs, some ovoviviparous species give birth to live young, for example skinks (*Chalcides* spp.) and vipers (*Vipera* spp.). In many species the temperature at which the eggs are incubated determines the sex of the young, with higher temperatures generally producing females.

Tortoises, Terrapins and Turtles

As a general rule, tortoises are strictly terrestrial, terrapins (see page 65) are semi-aquatic creatures of freshwater habitats and turtles are marine species that spend most of their lives at sea and only come ashore to lay their eggs. Five species of turtle have been recorded in Spanish coastal waters, by far the most common of which is the Loggerhead Turtle (*Caretta caretta*), although the only species known to lay its eggs on a Spanish beach in recent times is the Green Turtle (*Chelonia mydas*), with a clutch hatching successfully in Almería in 2001.

Two species of tortoise are found in Spain – typically in hot, dry localities – both of which are predominantly herbivorous, although they are not averse to snacking on carrion or the odd unwary invertebrate. Spur-thighed Tortoises (*Testudo graeca*) occur in just two widely separated nuclei in mainland Spain, Doñana in the south-west and the arid badlands of Almería

BELOW Over-collecting by the pet trade has severely depleted the Spanish populations of Spur-thighed Tortoises.

ABOVE Mediterranean Chameleons have an incredible talent for colour coordination with their surroundings.

when it is grasped by a predator (a process known as autonomy). Although the appendage usually regenerates, the replacement may not fit quite as well.

Mediterranean Chameleon

Although recent studies suggest that the Mediterranean Chameleon (*Chamaeleo chamaeleon*) was introduced to Spain and Portugal from north-west Morocco, in some populations this is thought to have taken place around 3,000 years ago. Today the species is distributed right along the southern Iberian coast, from the Portuguese Algarve to Almería, and is frequently found in gardens and allotments near the sea, although its preferred habitat is Stone Pine (*Pinus pinea*) forests with a White Broom (*Retama monosperma*) understorey on coastal sands.

Chameleons really are the most outlandish creatures, with swivelling 'gun-turret' eyes that can be moved independently, long, protractile tongues and the ability to change their skin colour both to blend in with their surroundings and to communicate their reproductive status. The Mediterranean Chameleon's body is flattened from side to side rather than from top to bottom, as is the norm for all other European reptiles. Its tail is amazingly prehensile and its five toes are arranged in a rather clumsy pincer-like formation, two directed forwards and three backwards. As these morphological features suggest, Mediterranean Chameleons spend most of their lives scrambling around in bushes, but as they are relatively slow-moving they often fall prey to other arboreal creatures such as Horseshoe Whip Snakes (*Hemorrhois hippocrepidis*) and Montpellier Snakes (*Malpolon monspessulanus*), as well as to domestic cats.

and Murcia in the south-east, as well as on the Balearic island of Mallorca, where they were almost certainly introduced in historic times. Native Spanish populations of Hermann's Tortoise (*T. hermanni*) are confined to the province of Girona (Catalunya), with the Mallorcan and Menorcan enclaves once again being considered to derive from introductions, albeit around 3,000 years ago. Spur-thighed Tortoises, as their name suggests, sport a horny spur on the back of each hind leg and have just one supracaudal shell plate above the tail, while Hermann's Tortoises possess two supracaudal plates and a horny scale on the end of the tail, but no spurs.

Mating is a supremely undignified affair for male tortoises of both species, as the high, smooth shells of the females all too often resist their efforts to climb on board. Once successful, however, up to a dozen hard-shelled eggs are laid in a hole dug by the female in a sunny location. The miniscule babies, which are only 35 mm long and weigh about 10 g, emerge 2–3 months later, but do not reach maturity for almost a decade. Although Spur-thighed Tortoises have been known to live for up to 100 years in captivity, the oldest known individual in the wild in Doñana is only 43. Wild populations of both the Spanish tortoises are severely threatened by habitat destruction, forest fires and indiscriminate collecting for the pet trade.

Lizards

Spanish lizards display an incredible diversity of morphology, behaviour and lifestyle. Many have the ability to shed their tail

Legless Lizards

The only member of the family Amphisbaenidae to occur in Spain is the Iberian Worm Lizard (*Blanus cinereus*), whose world distribution is restricted to Mediterranean habitats in the Iberian Peninsula. Resembling a giant earthworm more than a lizard, this bizarre creature has a reddish-brown, cylindrical body up to 29 cm long, with a distinctly annular appearance. Iberian Worm Lizards lead a primarily subterranean existence, excavating tunnels and feeding underground. Their minute eyes are covered with scales, and it is thought that they detect their prey – chiefly ants and insect larvae – by sound and, to a lesser extent, by smell. Although little is known about the reproductive habits of this species, each female apparently lays just one extremely elongated egg 25–30 mm long and 5 mm wide, which takes 70–80 days to hatch.

By contrast, the Slow Worm (*Anguis fragilis*, family Anguidae), a widespread species in Europe, occurs principally in humid grasslands and forests in the northern reaches of the Iberian Peninsula. The adults are rather snake-like in appearance, but have very smooth, gleaming scales and closable eye-lids. Unlike snakes, however, both Slow Worms and Iberian Worm Lizards are able to shed their tails in order to escape from predators. Female Slow Worms typically give birth to an average of 11–12 live young, each of which is 5–10 cm long and has a distinctive cream-coloured back marked with a narrow dark central stripe.

Geckos

These lizards of the family Gekkonidae differ from other saurians in having large, cat-like eyes with vertical pupils, and also in being very vocal creatures that emit a wide variety of calls, ranging from squeaks to barks. Two species occur in mainland Spain and the Balearic Islands. The Turkish Gecko (*Hemidactylus turcicus*) has a circum-Mediterranean distribution, extending eastwards as far as India and Pakistan, but in Spain it is confined to lowlands in the south and east, although it was also introduced in historic times to Gran Canaria and Tenerife. Unlike most Spanish reptiles, Turkish Geckos are predominantly crepuscular and nocturnal, so they can only live at low altitudes in warm climates where the temperature is relatively high at night. They are frequently found in human habitations, even in large cities, loitering around lights at night in the hope of capturing nocturnal insects or spiders. Turkish Geckos are slender creatures rarely more than 12 cm long, with translucent, flesh-coloured skin that is sprinkled with tiny whitish tubercles. They are extremely fast and agile climbers, with adhesive pads on the tips of their toes that even allow them to cling to ceilings upside down.

The Moorish Gecko (*Tarentola mauritanica*) is a much plumper, more robust creature that reaches an average length of about 15 cm and has a large, triangular head. Distinctly flattened dorso-ventrally, its body is decorated with longitudinal rows of prominent, spiny tubercles, and its toes – which again bear adhesive pads – are markedly dilated towards the tips. The overall body colour is greyish-brown, although Moorish Geckos become darker when basking in the sun so as to absorb more heat, and are generally paler at night. With a natural distribution centred on the western Mediterranean region, including North Africa, Moorish Geckos are found across much of southern and eastern Iberia and the Balearic Islands, reaching altitudes of 2,350 m in Andalucía.

The Canary Islands are home to four further species of *Tarentola*, thought to be derived from African ancestors that colonized the archipelago on three separate occasions. All are rather similar in appearance to the Moorish Gecko, but usually

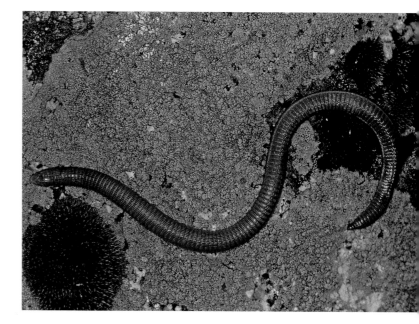

RIGHT, TOP Iberian Worm Lizards are typically pinkish, brown or grey, sometimes with a violet tinge.

RIGHT, CENTRE Although they are principally nocturnal, Moorish Geckos can sometimes be surprised while 'sun-bathing'.

RIGHT, BOTTOM The Gran Canaria Gecko is the smallest member of the genus *Tarentola* in Spain, with a head-and-body length of less than 6 cm.

ABOVE At a glance, the tiny, vestigial limbs of the Western Three-toed Skink are not visible, heightening its resemblance to a snake.

ABOVE Although widespread in Europe, in Spain the Common Wall Lizard is confined to Atlantic and montane habitats in the north.

somewhat smaller. The East Canary Gecko (*T. angustimentalis*) is confined to Lanzarote and Fuerteventura, the Gran Canaria Gecko (*T. boettgeri*) occurs on Gran Canaria, El Hierro and in the Portuguese Selvagens archipelago (with a different subspecies recognized for each), the Tenerife Gecko (*T. delalandii*) is found on Tenerife and La Palma, and the La Gomera Gecko (*T. gomerensis*) is restricted to the island of the same name.

All the Spanish geckos produce just 1–2 eggs per clutch, which they bury in loose soil, with the temperature of the substratum determining both the length of the incubation period and the sex of the young. Several clutches may be laid each year in favourable conditions.

Skinks

Like Slow Worms, skinks (family Scincidae) are smooth and shiny, with more or less cylindrical bodies, small heads and reduced limbs, the latter possibly an adaptation to a life spent amid thick vegetation. Leaving aside the six species of skink that occur in the African enclaves of Ceuta, Melilla and the nearby Chafarinas archipelago, Spain is home to five members of the genus *Chalcides*, all of which are predominantly diurnal and ovoviviparous, each female giving birth to a small number of fully formed young.

As is the case for the geckos, the Canaries archipelago is endowed with three species of skink whose ranges do not overlap. As their vernacular names suggest, Gran Canaria Skinks (*C. sexlineatus*), which often have blue or green tails, are confined to Gran Canaria, East Canary Skinks (*C. simonyi*) are found only on Fuerteventura and Lanzarote, and West Canary Skinks (*C. viridanus*) occur on Tenerife, El Hierro and La Gomera. It is thought that the Canary Island skinks are the result of two separate waves of invasion from western Morocco, the first giving rise to the East Canary Skink and the second bringing the ancestors of the two more westerly species. Curiously, La Palma seems to have missed out on the

skink incursions altogether. For the most part, the Canary Islands skinks are secretive creatures inhabiting hot, dry habitats at low altitudes, although the Gran Canaria Skink is also known to occur amid the volcanic peaks of the island at more than 1,800 m above sea level.

Two additional species of skink can be found on the Spanish mainland. Bedriaga's Skink (*C. bedriagai*) is an Iberian endemic, distributed across much of the Mediterranean climatic zone at low altitudes, while the Western Three-toed Skink (*C. striatus*), also known from France and Italy, prefers more humid habitats in the north and west of the peninsula. The Western Three-toed Skink has the tiniest limbs of all the Spanish species, and is also much the longest – exceptionally more than 40 cm – resembling a slender, burnished snake as it wriggles through the grass.

Lacertid Lizards

With more than 30 native species, typical lizards of the family Lacertidae make up by far the largest part of the Spanish reptilian fauna. A number of predominantly Euro-Siberian species only just creep into the northern reaches of Spain. These include the Sand Lizard (*Lacerta agilis*), Viviparous Lizard (*Zootoca vivipara*) and Common Wall Lizard (*Podarcis muralis*). The genera *Iberolacerta* and *Gallotia* are restricted to the Iberian Peninsula and the Canary Islands respectively.

Canary Islands Lizards

The genus *Gallotia* contains some of the biggest lacertid lizards in the world. Almost certainly deriving from individuals of north-west African origin, it seems that they spread across the archipelago over a period of several million years, evolving into seven distinct species en route. Owing to the dearth of native predators, some were able to grow extremely large, especially the island-specific Gran Canaria Giant Lizard (*Gallotia stehlini*), El Hierro Giant Lizard (*G. simonyi*) and La

ABOVE Abundant in most habitats within its range, the Tenerife Lizard is absent only from the *laurisilva* and land above 3,000 m.

ABOVE During the breeding season, male Schreiber's Green Lizards acquire a dazzling blue head to offset their smart green livery.

Gomera Giant Lizard (*G. bravoana*). Today the males of these substantial lizards often exceed half a metre in length and can weigh more than a kilogram, but fossil evidence shows that individuals almost twice this size existed before the islands were colonized by man, when the fragile natural equilibrium was destroyed by the introduction of dogs, cats and rats.

Less robust members of the genus are the Atlantic Lizard (*G. atlantica*), the only species found on Fuerteventura and Lanzarote, Boettger's Lizard (*G. caesaris*), from El Hierro and La Gomera, Tenerife Lizard (*G. galloti*), found on Tenerife and La Palma, and the island-specific Tenerife Speckled Lizard (*G. intermedia*), first described from the Teno peninsula in 2000.

Habitat loss and introduced predators have had a severe impact on the La Gomera and El Hierro Giant Lizards and the Tenerife Speckled Lizard, which today are confined to remote, sparsely vegetated coastal cliffs. Fewer than 300 El Hierro Giant Lizards remain in the wild, inhabiting an area of less than 10 sq km, while the La Gomera Giant Lizard is in an even worse state, with a wild population numbering just 40 individuals and occupying less than 2 ha. By contrast, the remaining four species are abundant and equally at home in all the open, sunny habitats present on their respective islands, from sea level up to the highest peaks.

Rock Lizards

The genus *Iberolacerta* is a relatively recent concept, deriving from a revision of several Iberian taxa previously placed in the genus *Lacerta* following extensive DNA and chromosome studies. Seven species are currently recognized, including three with very localized distributions in the high Pyrenees on the Franco–Spanish border: the Aran Rock Lizard (*I. aranica*), Aurelio's Rock Lizard (*I. aurelioi*) and the Pyrenean Rock Lizard (*I. bonnali*). The remaining four species are all Iberian endemics. The Iberian Rock Lizard (*I. monticola*) is restricted to the mountains of north-western Iberia and central Portugal, *I.*

cyreni is confined to Spain's Sistema Central, *I. martinezricae* is unique to the Sierra de Francia, on the Salamanca–Cáceres border, and *I. galani*, first described in 2006, is endemic to the Montes de León.

All the *Iberolacerta* species are medium-sized, fairly robust lizards, generally boasting black reticulation or stripes on a green or brown ground colour. They are particularly associated with rock formations and screes above the tree-line, with the Pyrenean Rock Lizard being recorded from altitudes of up to 3,000 m, although the Iberian Rock Lizard is also found right down to sea level in Galicia. Because high-mountain environments are extremely cold for much of the year, these rock lizards are active for just a few months in high summer, and the females rarely produce more than one clutch of eggs each season.

Green Lizards

Europe's largest lacertid is the predominantly green Ocellated Lizard (*Timon lepidus*) – it is greyish in the badlands of south-eastern Spain – the males of which can attain a massive 70 cm from nose to tail. It is distributed throughout the Iberian Peninsula and across southern France into north-west Italy. Superficially similar green species are Schreiber's Green Lizard (*Lacerta schreiberi*), found only in the northern and western reaches of Iberia, often close to running water, and the Western Green Lizard (*L. bilineata*), a Western European species that in Spain is confined to the northern reaches. Somewhat smaller than the Ocellated Lizard, the males of both species develop bright blue heads in the breeding season, but while Western Green Lizards possess green tails, in Schreiber's Green Lizard this appendage is usually brown.

Wall Lizards

Wall lizards of the genus *Podarcis* are represented in Spain by seven fairly small native species, two of which are confined to the Balearic Islands. Lilford's Wall Lizard (*P. lilfordi*) was once

ABOVE Iberian Wall Lizards can be distinguished from Common Wall Lizards by the absence of reticulation on the throat.

commonplace on Menorca and Mallorca, but disappeared from both main islands some 2,000 years ago with the arrival of man and the introduction of terrestrial predators. Today Lilford's Wall Lizard is restricted to offshore islets and the Cabrera archipelago where, in a superb example of divergent evolution as a result of geographic isolation, some 23 distinct subspecies have been described, about half of which exhibit melanic colouration. This species is also notable for displaying the highest population densities of any reptile in the world, with up to 32,000 individuals having been recorded in a single hectare.

The other Balearic member of the genus is the Ibiza Wall Lizard (*P. pityusensis*). It is restricted to the islands of Ibiza and Formentera, plus their neighbouring islets, and again displays

BELOW Photographed in the Sierra de Aracena, this Large Psammodromus probably pertains to the new species *Psammodromus manuelae*.

considerable levels of subspeciation and high population densities. The Columbretes Wall Lizard (*P. atra*) is another island-dwelling member of the genus, in this case being unique to the Columbretes archipelago, which is located some 56 km off the Valencian coast.

In mainland Spain, the Iberian Wall Lizard (*P. hispanica*) is by far the most abundant and widespread species, also extending into south-eastern France. By contrast, Bocage's Wall Lizard (*P. bocagei*) is an Iberian endemic confined to the north-western reaches of the peninsula. To the south of the River Duero, this species is replaced by the very similar Carbonell's Wall Lizard (*P. carbonelli*), which only just extends eastwards from Portugal into the Spanish provinces of Salamanca, Cáceres and Huelva.

Psammodromuses

Until recently, only two species of the genus *Psammodromus* – fairly easily identified on account of their extremely long, slender tails – were known from Europe, both with distributions centred on the Iberian Peninsula: Spanish and Large Psammodromuses (*P. hispanicus* and *P. algirus*). Recent DNA studies, however, have revealed that the North African *P. algirus* is not in fact the same creature as those found in Iberia, so two new species were described in 2006 – *P. manuelae* from the area to the west and north of the Guadalquivir, and *P. jeanneae* from the south and east of this river – although the geographical boundary between the two in central and northern Spain has yet to be determined.

Other Lacerid Lizards

Other Spanish lacerid lizards of note include the Spiny-footed Lizard (*Acanthodactylus erythrurus*), a long-toed Afro-Iberian endemic species that is characteristic of dry habitats in the Mediterranean climatic zone, particularly coastal sand dunes, and the endemic Spanish Algyroides (*Algyroides marchi*), whose world population is confined to shady rocky outcrops at 1,000–1,700 m in the south-eastern *sierras* of Cazorla, Segura and Alcaraz.

Snakes

Two snake families occur in Spain: 'typical' snakes of the family Colubridae, and vipers of the family Viperidae. Among the Spanish colubrids, only Montpellier Snakes (*Malpolon monspessulanus*) and Western False Smooth Snakes (*Macroprotodon brevis*) possess fangs, located at the rear of the jaw rather than at the front, as in the vipers.

Colubrid Snakes

By far the largest of the ten Spanish colubrids is the Montpellier Snake, which is known to reach 240 cm in length and can weigh more than 3 kg. Widespread in southern Europe, and present in all but the extreme north of the Iberian Peninsula, this species is distinguished by its prominent 'eyebrows', overhanging large eyes with round pupils and uniformly olive-green body. Although fairly aggressive, the Montpellier Snake is regarded as relatively harmless to humans as it needs a very firm grip for the rear-mounted fangs to operate. Even so, its venom is not strong enough to cause more than a passing numbness and swelling.

Widespread European colubrids found in Spain are the Grass Snake (*Natrix natrix*), which is rarely found far from water, Aesculapian and Western Whip Snakes (*Zamenis longissimus* and *Hierophis viridiflavus*), both present only in the extreme north, and Smooth Snake (*Coronella austriaca*), the latter rather atypical of the family in that the females give birth to live young rather than laying eggs.

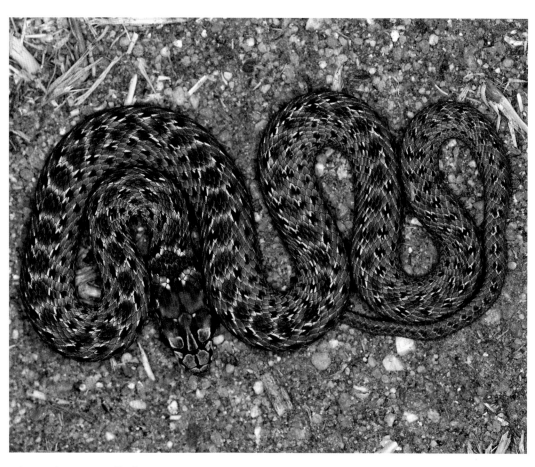

By contrast, Ladder Snakes (*Rhinechis scalaris*), so called on account of the barred appearance of the juveniles, have a predominantly Iberian world distribution, as do Horseshoe Whip Snakes (*Hemorrhois hippocrepidis*), which often hunt and take refuge in buildings. The Western False Smooth Snake, a species possibly introduced from North Africa, is unusual in that it preys primarily on other reptiles, particularly Iberian Worm Lizards, *Psammodromus* spp., and Bedriaga's Skinks, as well as juvenile snakes, including those of its own species.

ABOVE Unlike the uniformly coloured adults, juvenile Montpellier Snakes are marked with a complex design of black-and-white spots.
BELOW Adult Horseshoe Whip Snakes are highly predatory reptiles, actively hunting down passerines, rodents and even bats.

Vipers

European members of the Viperidae are distinguished by their vertical pupils and strongly keeled dorsal scales. Three species are found in Spain, all of which are venomous, feeding principally on small mammals, but also taking reptiles, amphibians and small birds. Vipers are generally fairly heavy-bodied snakes with roughly triangular heads and short tails that taper off abruptly, and they often sport a prominent zigzag dorsal line; the females give birth to live young.

The Asp Viper (*Vipera aspis*) is a central European species that only just extends into north-east Spain, occurring in the Pyrenees, where it reaches altitudes of almost 3,000 m, and the eastern Cordillera Cantábrica, while Seoane's Viper (*V. seoanei*) is largely confined to northern Spain, just extending into Portugal and south-west France. Finally, Lataste's Viper (*V. latasti*) is an Afro-Iberian endemic that occurs across much of Spain except the far north. It is distinguished from the other two Spanish vipers in having a pronounced nose-horn.

BIRDS

The birdlife of Spain is extraordinarily rich, with more than 520 species cited to date, of which 337 breed in the country. Of these, 49 species have been introduced, although only a few are firmly established in the wild, for example Monk Parakeets (*Myiopsitta monachus*), Waxbills (*Estrilda astrild*) and Red Avadavats (*Amandava amandava*). Of the 288 native birds that breed in Spain, more than 90 per cent do so on a regular basis.

ABOVE Around one-fifth of the world population of Cinereous Vultures lives in Spain, numbering almost 2,000 pairs.

Of the 40 European birds considered to be of global conservation concern (SPEC 1) by BirdLife International, five are present only in Spanish territory. The Balearic Shearwater (*Puffinus mauretanicus*) is endemic to the archipelago of the same name, and a further four species are unique to the Canaries, namely Bolle's Pigeon (*Columba bollii*), the Laurel Pigeon (*C. junoniae*), the Canary Islands Stonechat (*Saxicola dacotiae*) and the Blue Chaffinch (*Fringilla teydea*).

In addition, significant proportions of the European breeding populations of a further nine SPEC 1 species are found in Spanish territory:

Marbled Teal (*Marmaronetta angustirostris*) Roughly 50 per cent of the European population.

White-headed Duck (*Oxyura leucocephala*) Approximately a quarter of the global population.

Cinereous Vulture (*Aegypius monachus*) 85 per cent of the European population.

Spanish Imperial Eagle (*Aquila adalberti*) Virtually the whole global population (see also box, page 127).

Lesser Kestrel (*Falco naumanni*) About 60 per cent of the European population.

Little Bustard (*Tetrax tetrax*) Approximately half of the European population.

Houbara Bustard (*Chlamydotis undulata*) All the European breeding birds, as subspecies *C. u. fuerteventurae*.

Great Bustard (*Otis tarda*) Roughly 60 per cent of the European population.

Audouin's Gull (*Larus audouinii*) About 90 per cent of the world population of this Mediterranean species.

Spain also harbours important breeding populations of a number of essentially European birds with an unfavourable conservation status on the continent (SPEC 2), including Black and White Storks (*Ciconia ciconia* and *C. nigra*), Eleonora's Falcon (*Falco eleonorae*), Red-legged Partridge (*Alectoris rufa*), Scops Owl (*Otus scops*), the Macaronesian endemic Plain Swift (*Apus unicolor*), European Roller (*Coracias garrulus*), Green Woodpecker (*Picus viridis*), Wood Lark (*Lullula arborea*), Woodchat Shrike (*Lanius senator*), Black-eared Wheatear (*Oenanthe hispanica*), Dartford Warbler (*Sylvia undata*), Bonelli's Warbler (*Phylloscopus bonelli*) and Corn Bunting (*Miliaria calandra*).

ABOVE Although Iberian Azure-winged Magpies feed primarily on invertebrates, they often frequent picnic sites in search of scraps.

Mainland Endemics

Although no bird species occur exclusively in mainland Spain, the Iberian Azure-winged Magpie (*Cyanopica cooki*) is unique to the Iberian Peninsula. The presence of this corvid in the Iberian Peninsula was for many years a mystery, as its nearest known relative – the Azure-winged Magpie (*C. cyanus*) – is found some 8,000 km away in eastern Asia. For many years it was thought that the Iberian magpies belonged to this Asian species and were possibly introduced to Spain and Portugal by mariners. At the end of the 20th century, however, fossil remains were discovered in Gibraltar in strata dating from almost 45,000 years ago, indicating that the birds were present in the peninsula during the Pleistocene glaciations. Recent DNA analyses have confirmed that the Spanish and Portuguese birds are sufficiently distinct to merit specific status.

The Spanish distribution of the Iberian Azure-winged Magpie is centred on Extremadura and western Andalucía, particularly in *dehesas* and open pine forests, although it appears to be expanding slowly and now extends as far east as Soria and Albacete. The global population is in the region of a quarter of a million birds.

Spanish Capercaillies

A number of more widespread but largely sedentary European birds have evolved into unique subspecies in mainland Spain, most notably the Capercaillie (*Tetrao urogallus cantabricus*) of the high-level beech forests of the Cordillera Cantábrica. This magnificent member of the grouse family (Tetraonidae) has undergone a spectacular reduction in numbers – in the order of 70 per cent – in the past 30 years. Today only some 220 occupied leks (territories where the male birds display in order to attract females) remain, which are confined to an area of just 1,700 sq km in the western Cordillera Cantábrica, principally in Asturias and northern León.

Habitat destruction is an important contributory factor in this decline. Given that beech leaves are of very limited nutritional value, the adult birds depend heavily on the understorey of Bilberry (*Vaccinium myrtillus*) for food, and it also provides cover for the young chicks. Unfortunately there is an increas-

BELOW During its late-winter courtship display, the male Capercaillie displays its 'beard' and fans its tail in order to impress females.

ABOVE Like most pelagic seabirds, the Balearic Shearwater feeds mainly on fish and cephalopods, often following fishing boats.

ing tendency to graze domestic livestock in these forests, thus destroying the ground layer and both exposing the chicks to cold spring rains – hypothermia is a very real threat – and obliging the birds to seek food in peripheral areas, where they are all too vulnerable to predation and even poaching.

Although the distribution of the Pyrenean Capercaillie (*T. u. aquitanicus*) also extends onto the French flanks of the

BELOW The Canary Islands Stonechat feeds primarily on insects – either flying or terrestrial – which it locates from a convenient perch.

Pyrenees, it too is in a bad way, with fewer than 700 male territories remaining on the Spanish side of the chain. More than 99 per cent of these are located in the central and eastern Pyrenees, with the tiny Navarra population in the west now completely isolated and thus susceptible to inbreeding.

Balearic Specialities

The Balearic archipelago is home to two birds that breed nowhere else in the world: the Balearic Shearwater (*Puffinus mauretanicus*) and the Balearic Warbler (*Sylvia balearica*), the latter recently separated taxonomically from Marmora's Warbler (*S. sarda*), which occurs on the other western Mediterranean islands. Curiously, the Balearic Warbler is absent from Menorca, but on the remaining islands – including Cabrera and Sa Dragonera – it is predominantly associated with low *maquis*, occurring up to 1,200 m in the Serra de Tramuntana. The global population of this species is estimated at around 18,000 pairs and appears to be relatively stable.

Unfortunately, the same cannot be said of the Balearic Shearwater. Like other members of the family Procellariidae, this species is highly pelagic – spending most of its life at sea and coming ashore only to breed – with poorly developed legs set far back on the body, giving it an extremely awkward gait on land. Balearic Shearwaters breed on remote sea cliffs and offshore islets, usually in colonies, utilizing natural caves and crevices between rocks. Each nest contains just a single egg, and the parents usually visit the breeding grounds at night. The global population of Balearic Shearwater has declined dramatically in recent years – principally due to nest predation by rats and feral cats – with a 2001 census discovering a meagre 1,750–2,125 pairs. Rigorous control of predators and the protection under European law of all known nesting sites have allowed the Balearic Shearwater population to recover somewhat in recent years: 8,000-plus individuals, including 2,300 breeding pairs, were located in 2006.

Unique Taxa of the Canary Islands

Not surprisingly, the high degree of geographical isolation experienced by the Canary Islands has led to the evolution of no less than six endemic bird species: Bolle's Pigeon (*Columba bollii*), the Laurel Pigeon (*C. junoniae*), Canary Islands Stonechat (*Saxicola dacotiae*), Canary Islands Kinglet (*Regulus teneriffae*), Canary Islands Chiffchaff (*Phylloscopus canariensis*) and Blue Chaffinch (*Fringilla teydea*). Three other Canary Islands species occur exclusively in Macaronesia: the Island

Canary (*Serinus canaria*), Berthelot's Pipit (*Anthus bertholotii*) and the Plain Swift (*Apus unicolor*), while the essentially North African Barbary Falcon (*Falco pelegrinoides*) has its only European breeding grounds here.

With a global population of about 2,000 individuals, the Laurel Pigeon – sometimes known as the White-tailed Laurel Pigeon on account of the broad, off-white band at the end of its tail – is confined to the western Canary Islands, particularly La Palma and La Gomera. Because it nests on the ground, its eggs and chicks are especially vulnerable to predation by introduced rats and cats. In Tenerife, for example, almost three-quarters of the nests studied between 1993 and 1997 failed for this reason. Bolle's Pigeon, which nests high in the canopy of the *laurisilva*, is in a much better position to avoid nest predation; maybe for this reason, its world population today is thought to number about 6,000 birds, almost half of which are located on La Palma.

The endangered Canary Islands Stonechat is unique to the island of Fuerteventura, where it inhabits moderately vegetated habitats, particularly on steep, stony slopes in *barrancos*; it is sometimes known as the Fuerteventura Chat. A 1985 census put the world population at 650–850 pairs, but because this species constructs its nest close to the ground, introduced predators are once again responsible for the failure of about half of all breeding attempts, so that its numbers are almost certainly much lower today.

By contrast, populations of the Canary Islands Kinglet – sometimes referred to as the Tenerife Goldcrest – and the Canary Islands Chiffchaff appear to be in reasonably good shape at the moment. Both of these diminutive passerines are sedentary birds, associated primarily with laurel and pine forests in the western Canaries, although the latter's distribution extends as far east as Gran Canaria.

Unfortunately the same cannot be said of the Blue Chaffinch, the most emblematic bird of the archipelago's Canary Pine (*Pinus canariensis*) forests. The Gran Canary race (*Fringilla teydea polatzeki*) is probably at greatest risk, with the July 2007 forest fire in its principal habitat having a devastating impact on the few hundred remaining birds, while the Tenerife race (*F. t. teydea*) is a little better off, with a world population numbering about a thousand pairs.

In addition, about 30 Canary Islands endemic subspecies have been described to date, many of which are severely threatened today. In the case of the Egyptian Vulture (*Neophron percnopterus majorensis*), fewer than 30 pairs remain on Fuerteventura, plus a single pair on Lanzarote and one on the islet of Alegranza, while the Barn Owl (*Tyto alba*

ABOVE The Canary Islands endemic subspecies of Egyptian Vulture has its stronghold on the island of Fuerteventura.

gracilirostris) of the eastern Canaries has an estimated world population of just 150 pairs. In contrast to their relatives on the Spanish mainland, these Barn Owls are rarely associated with human edifices, instead breeding primarily in remote *barrancos* and volcanic craters, or on coastal cliffs. The Raven (*Corvus corax canariensis*) is found in similar habitats throughout the Canary Islands, but even so its world population is not thought to exceed a few hundred pairs. It is particularly at risk on Gran Canaria, where the population has decreased from 160 to 20–25 pairs in the last decade.

In the past decade, the wild Canary Islands' population of the Lesser Short-toed Lark (*Calandrella rufescens rufescens*) has been reduced to just one or two pairs scattered across a few hectares in northern Tenerife, so that the future of this, the nominate subspecies, hangs on the breeding success – or otherwise – of a small captive population. The race *C. r. polatzeki* – endemic to Gran Canaria, Lanzarote and Fuerteventura – is not quite in such dire straits, but the abandonment of traditional agricultural practices and insensitive tourist development are clearly having a negative impact on its population.

Other endangered Canary Islands endemic subspecies are the Houbara Bustard (*Chlamydotis undulata fuerteventurae*), confined to Fuerteventura and Lanzarote (including La Graciosa), with an estimated population of about 1,000 indi-

ABOVE Trumpeter Finches have enormously strong beaks for cracking hard seeds; red in the male but dull orange in the female (depicted).
BELOW The sleek, glossy plumage of the Spotless Starling serves to distinguish it from the Common Starling (*Sturnus vulgaris*).

viduals, and two races of the Eurasian Thick-knee or Stone Curlew (*Burhinus oedicnemus*). The subspecies *B. o. distinctus* is found only on the western islands of the archipelago, particularly Gran Canaria and El Hierro, where its population is in the region of 300–400 pairs. Replacement of its preferred habitat – stony, arid badlands – with banana plantations would appear to constitute the principal threat. The other subspecies, *B. o. insularum*, occurs only on Fuerteventura, Lanzarote and the islets to the north, and has an estimated population of around 1,500 pairs.

Afro-Iberian Birds

Because of its proximity to Africa, it is not surprising that mainland Iberia harbours the only Western European breeding populations of a number of birds with a more southerly world range, notably the White-headed Duck (*Oxyura leucocephala*), Black-shouldered Kite (*Elanus caeruleus*), Small Buttonquail (*Turnix sylvatica*), Red-knobbed Coot (*Fulica cristata*), White-rumped Swift (*Apus caffer*), Red-necked Nightjar (*Caprimulgus ruficollis*), Dupont's Lark (*Chersophilus duponti*), Black Wheatear (*Oenanthe leucura*) and Trumpeter Finch (*Bucanetes githagineus zedlitzi*), although the Canary Islands also host an endemic subspecies (*B. g. amantum*) of the latter.

Most of these birds are present in Spain in some numbers, with the exception of the almost mythical Small Buttonquail. Formerly known as the Andalusian Hemipode, this quail-like, ground-nesting bird is such a retiring creature that no one is sure whether it still breeds in Spain or not. The species is almost certainly extinct in Portugal, Algeria and Tunisia, but there is a chance that small enclaves persist in its former breeding grounds in the Doñana marshes.

Moving North As Temperatures Rise

It is surely not coincidence that as global climate change makes itself felt, several essentially African birds have ventured north across the Straits of Gibraltar to colonize Iberia. The White-rumped Swift's northwards expansion into Spain and Portugal is a fairly recent occurrence, dating from the mid-1960s, although thus far it has reached no further than Extremadura, with the majority of the 100-odd breeding pairs located in Cádiz and Córdoba (Andalucía). These swifts have the curious habit of parasitizing the 'igloo-shaped' nests of Red-rumped Swallows (*Hirundo daurica*), making their occupancy known by adorning the entrances with tufts of white feathers. Even more recently, the Little Swift (*Apus affinis*) was first discovered nesting on the coast of Cádiz in 1995, with three confirmed breeding localities today.

Similarly, the first Spanish breeding records of the North African race of the Trumpeter Finch (*Bucanetes githagineuszedlitzi*) date from 1972, in Almería. Since this time its population has increased to about 800 pairs and its range has expanded northwards to reach Alacant and the Hoya de

Guadix in Granada. Small flocks of this tubby finch – named for its rather nasal call – typically inhabit dry, cliff-lined gullies in south-eastern Spain, the breeding males easily identified by their thick red beaks and pinkish plumage.

It would seem that the Black-shouldered Kite is also taking advantage of increasing temperatures across southern Europe. For many years south-western Spain and Portugal played host to Europe's only breeding population of this elegant, red-eyed raptor, but a slow northwards expansion since the 1970s has recently taken it across the border into south-west France. The European population ranges from 810 to 2,000 pairs, varying with fluctuations in rodent numbers. The majority of Spanish Black-shouldered Kites breed in Castilla y León and Extremadura.

Having probably become extinct in France at the end of the last century, the Black Wheatear is nowadays confined to Iberia and North Africa. Europe's breeding population of this unmistakable thrush – soot-black with a white tail – lies in the region of 16,000 pairs, the great majority of which occupy hot, dry habitats in the mountains of southern and eastern Spain.

Although much more abundant, the Spotless Starling (*Sturnus unicolor*) breeds only in the western Mediterranean region, both on the African and European shores. With an essentially Iberian distribution in Europe – it also breeds on Corsica, Sardinia and Sicily – it has again been noted moving northwards in the last half-century, reaching south-eastern France in 1989.

Red-knobbed Coots and White-headed Ducks

By contrast, the lack of rain over much of southern Spain in recent years is having a negative impact on many wetland birds. Indiscriminate drainage and pollution had already affected Red-knobbed Coot populations in Iberia, leading to the bird's extinction in Portugal in the mid-19th century and marked decline across Spain during the 20th century. The 21st century has seen a series of extremely dry years, which have affected water levels in many of the coot's most suitable breeding localities. As a result, despite the captive breeding and release of almost 500 birds in 1999–2004, fewer than 250 wild breeding individuals remain in Spain today, with a stronghold in the Lagunas de Cádiz.

The White-headed Duck is a distinctive little stiff-tail, the breeding males being easily identified by their bright blue bills. At the end of the 20th century, it was the protagonist of one of the major success stories of Spanish conservation initiatives, undergoing a spectacular recovery from just 22 individuals in 1977 to about 2,300 birds in 2002. Unfortunately, the lack of rain in recent years is reflected by the 2006 census turning up just 1,500 breeding individuals dispersed across 25 wetlands, principally in Andalucía and Castilla–La Mancha.

ABOVE The Red-knobbed Coot's 'knobs' are only obvious during the breeding season, and are absent altogether in young birds.

The Spanish White-headed Ducks have an additional problem to contend with: the American Ruddy Duck (*Oxyura jamaicensis*) was introduced to wildfowl collections in Great Britain in the 1960s, from whence it has proceeded to colonize much of Western Europe, first arriving in Spain in the 1980s. This New World species is so similar to the White-headedDuck

BELOW Only male White-headed Ducks have completely white heads, with a swollen bill that turns bright blue in the breeding season.

ABOVE Unlike most members of the Alaudidae, male Dupont's Larks are just as happy singing from a terrestrial perch as from the sky.
BELOW A pair of Marbled Teal on the margins of the Laguna de Miguel Esteban, in the Biosphere Reserve of La Mancha Húmeda.

Duck that the two are able to interbreed, producing fertile hybrid offspring that are an obvious threat to the genetic integrity of the much rarer White-headed Duck. In order to combat this hazard, selective hunting of both Ruddy Duck and hybrids has been taking place in Spain since 1992, while a breeding nucleus of captive-bred White-headed Ducks was progressively introduced to the Albufera de Mallorca in the 1990s, in the hopes that an isolated island population would be easier to protect from genetic contamination.

Dupont's Lark

Spain is the only country in Europe in which Dupont's Lark can be found, the remainder of its population occurring in the Mediterranean hinterland of North Africa. It is a secretive species that prefers to run and hide rather than to take flight when disturbed, and is distinguished from other European members of the Alaudidae by its long, down-curved bill. The world population of Dupont's Larks is not thought to exceed 15,000 pairs, of which about 2,000 pairs occur in Spain, nowadays confined to 14 widely separated enclaves. By far the larger part of the Spanish population breeds either on the high plateaux of the Sistema Ibérico – particularly in the province of Soria – or in arid enclaves in the Ebro Basin: Los Monegros, Belchite and the Bardenas Reales. Dupont's Larks are highly sensitive to intensification of land use, particularly ploughing either for cereal crops or to plant pines trees. This destroys the low *garrigue* on which they depend for food and shelter, and the smaller enclaves are considered to be at serious risk.

Best Place in Europe to See

Mainland Spain is a particularly good place to track down some of Europe's most emblematic and eye-catching birds.

Greater Flamingoes

About 30 per cent of the western Mediterranean population of Greater Flamingoes (*Phoenicopterus roseus*) breeds in Spain,

although fluctuating water levels produce considerable annual variations in numbers. The largest and best-known colony occupies the shallow, hyper-saline lagoon of Fuente de Piedra, in central Andalucía, which in some years hosts an incredible 20,000-odd pairs. In recent years, however, either when water levels at Fuente de Piedra have been too low, or when the lagoon is at full occupancy, small satellite breeding enclaves have been established in Doñana, the Ebro Delta, El Hondo, the Salinas de Santa Pola and the Laguna de Pétrola.

Greater Flamingoes possess baleen-like filters in the bill against which the fleshy tongue is pressed in order to sieve small aquatic invertebrates from the water. They feed primarily on the crustacean *Artemia salina*, whose flesh contains the red pigment responsible for the pink plumage of the birds. Well-fed birds are the most brightly coloured, thus indicating that they make the most desirable mates. The adults feed primarily at night, often in wetlands several hundred kilometres distant, and return to the colony at daybreak to feed their chicks. Each pair rears just one chick a year, which is nourished with a remarkable bright-red goo known as 'flamingo milk' secreted by glands in the crops of both parents.

ABOVE Greater Flamingoes are able to feed even in deep water, as can be seen here in the Lagunas de Alcázar de San Juan.

Marbled Teal and Purple Swamp-hen

About half of Europe's breeding population of the Marbled Teal (*Marmaronetta angustirostris*) nests in Spain, primarily in Doñana, the Cañada de Las Norias, in Almería, and inland wetlands of the País Valencià, although the population rarely exceeds 200 pairs. Perhaps because it occupies shallow, seasonal lagoons, which often evaporate before breeding can take place, this diminutive, distinctively patterned duck has evolved a number of adaptations to assure that reproduction is successful when conditions are right. Marbled Teal become sexually mature after just a single year and have the largest clutch size of any member of the Anatidae, averaging a dozen eggs. The chicks are cared for assiduously by the female, so that almost all fledge successfully. As a result, the population undergoes dramatic fluctuations according to the wetness – or otherwise – of the season.

The Purple Swamp-hen (*Porphyrio porphyrio*), a huge red-billed, red-legged rail with glossy, bluish-purple plumage –

With a wingspan of up to 295 cm, this is the largest of the Spanish vultures, and in contrast to the remaining three (cliff-breeding) species, it opts to nest in the tops of evergreen oaks and pines. Its principal stronghold is south-western and central Spain, particularly Extremadura, but a small, isolated nucleus also persists on the Balearic island of Mallorca. Although the census data would appear to indicate a healthy Spanish population, about 500 Cinereous Vultures have died in the last 10 years as a result of consuming poisoned carcases put down in private hunting reserves to control predators.

At 10,000-plus pairs, the global population of the Lammergeier (*Gypaetus barbatus*) is similar to that of the Cinereous Vulture, but its European delegation is thought to number only about 610 pairs, with more than 200 of these ensconced in the French and Spanish Pyrenees. Sometimes known as the Bearded Vulture on account of the tufts of blackish bristles that extend downwards on either side of the bill, it is the only bird in the world known to feed almost exclusively on bones. In order to facilitate their ingestion, larger bones are repeatedly dropped from a height of 50–80 m to smash on the rocks below and thus expose the marrow. Not only are bones a rather scarce food resource; they are also not very nutritious, so Lammergeiers grow very slowly. The young take up to six months to leave the nest and do not reach sexual maturity until they are in their fifth year. Although the females usually lay two eggs, even if both hatch the older sibling kills the younger, so that only one ever leaves the nest.

ABOVE Lammergeiers patrol mountain hillsides on motionless wings for hours on end in search of carcases.

often referred to as the Purple Gallinule – is a much more cosmopolitan species, typical of tropical and subtropical wetlands in Asia, Africa and Australia. Nevertheless, a few discrete nuclei are also found around the Mediterranean, in Turkey, Sardinia and Portugal, but above all in Spain, which is estimated to harbour about 90 per cent of the European population. After suffering a serious decline in the first half of the 20th century that wiped out many European populations and relegated the Spanish birds to Doñana, the Purple Swamp-hen was deliberately introduced to the Aiguamolls de l'Empordà in 1989, and the Albuferas of Mallorca and València in 1991. Since then it has recolonized many wetlands under its own steam, particularly in Castilla–La Mancha and Extremadura, with recent estimates putting the number of Spanish birds at almost 7,000 breeding pairs and rising.

A Quartet of Vultures

A 2006 Spanish census located 35 colonies and 5 isolated nests of the Cinereous Vulture (*Aegypius monachus*), in total numbering 1,845 pairs and representing the lion's share of the European population of this majestic carrion-eater; in fact, the total world population is estimated at only 7,200–10,000 pairs.

Of the other two species of vulture that occur in Spain, the Griffon Vulture (*Gyps fulvus*) is present in extraordinary numbers, with more than 22,000 birds located in the most recent (1999) census. Absent as a breeding bird only from Galicia, the Mediterranean coast and the archipelagos, some river canyons of the *Meseta* are home to huge colonies of Griffon Vultures, notably the Hoces del Río Riaza and the Hoces del Río Duratón in Segovia (almost 400 pairs in each case), while the limestone labyrinth known as the Foces de la Sierra de Leyre, in Navarra, harbours around 700 breeding pairs.

Although the Egyptian Vulture (*Neophron percnopterus*) has disappeared from many of its more southerly outposts in the peninsula in the past 20 years, the mainland Spanish population is considered to be one of the most important in Europe – if not the world – numbering around 1,475 pairs in 2000. By far the smallest of all the vultures, adult birds are easily identified by their predominately white bodies, black flight feathers and diamond-shaped tails. The Egyptian Vulture is also the only

ABOVE The Griffon Vulture is only slightly smaller than its Cinereous relative, with a wingspan of up to 265 cm.

RIGHT Adults of the rare Bonelli's Eagle often sport a whitish mantle on their backs.

migratory species of the Iberian quartet, present between February and August, when it heads off to spend the winter in sub-Saharan Africa.

Eagles and Falcons

The most emblematic raptor of the Iberian peninsula is without a doubt the quasi-endemic Spanish Imperial Eagle (*Aquila adalberti*, see box, page 127). This said, almost 80 per cent of the European breeding population of Bonelli's Eagle (*Hieraaetus fasciatus*) also occurs in Spain, with the 2005 census turning up 733–768 pairs. Bonelli's Eagles are virtually confined to the Mediterranean region in the western Palaearctic, with the total European population barely exceeding a thousand pairs today and in manifest decline. They are most at home in hot, dry habitats, displaying a marked preference for rugged limestone hills that offer plenty of inaccessible nooks and crannies in which to nest, as well as a plentiful supply of medium-sized mammals and birds. Almost half of the Spanish population nests in Andalucía, with other important breeding enclaves located in the Mediterranean coastal ranges

ABOVE Golden Eagles feed primarily on mammals, from rodents to foxes, with Mediterranean birds particularly favouring rabbits.
LEFT Eleonora's Falcons often face into the wind and hover while they wait for migrating passerines to come into range.

and Extremadura. The unremitting decline of Bonelli's Eagle would seem to be due primarily to deaths among adult birds, with collisions with overhead power lines responsible for almost half the fatalities, closely followed by illegal hunting and deliberate poisoning, particularly by pigeon breeders. The spectacular reduction in European Rabbit (*Oryctolagus cuniculus*) populations has also taken its toll.

In addition, Spain is home to more than 20 per cent of Europe's Golden Eagles (*Aquila chrysaetos*), represented by a relatively stable population of about 1,450 pairs. Because this species is particularly affected by disturbance during the incubation of the eggs and early rearing of the young, it is associated mainly with the more remote valleys in Spain's major mountain ranges. The vast majority of Spanish Golden Eagles are cliff-breeders, but in the Ebro river valley it is not unknown for them to construct their nests in the tops of trees.

Spain's breeding population of Lesser Kestrels (*Falco naumanni*) is estimated to number in excess of 20,000 pairs. They are located for the most part in the central and south-western parts of the country, with an outlying enclave in the Ebro

SPANISH IMPERIAL EAGLE

The archetypal Mediterranean raptor, the Spanish Imperial Eagle (*Aquila adalberti*) is sometimes referred to simply as the Spanish Eagle, despite the fact that it formerly bred also in North Africa and Portugal, and has recently recolonized the latter. Because it relies on rabbits (see page 45) to provide a large proportion of its diet, the Spanish Imperial Eagle reached its nadir in the 1960s, with a world population estimated at around 50 pairs and a prominent position on both national and international Red Lists. Apart from the scarcity of its prey species, the main threats to its survival were wholesale habitat destruction, electrocution by power lines and indiscriminate poisoning.

Incredibly, however, this magnificent raptor – distinguished in its adult plumage by the pure white leading edge to its wing – has managed to elude the snapping jaws of extinction. In 2006, a census revealed the presence of 217 breeding pairs in the Iberian Peninsula, with about 75 per cent of their territories located in Extremadura, Castilla–La Mancha and Andalucía, and most of the remainder scattered across the Sistema Central in southern Castilla y León and northern Madrid. Due to measures such as the burying of power lines, supplementary feeding and attempts to boost rabbit populations, as well as strict penalties for the use of poison, more than 200 chicks have been born every year since 2003. Nevertheless, more than 80 per cent of young birds still die before they reach maturity, with electrocution responsible for more than half of these losses, so that the survival of the Spanish Imperial Eagle is not yet a foregone conclusion.

BELOW Spanish Imperial Eagles habitually construct their nests in the canopies of evergreen oaks and pines.

Depression. Although over much of its global range this small falcon is a cliff-breeding species, a large proportion of Spanish Lesser Kestrels nest in buildings, particularly ancient or ruined churches, even in city centres, occupying cavities under roof tiles or holes in walls. The birds breed in colonies, and can be seen hunting in groups over cereal fields and fallow land in search of both aerial and terrestial prey, especially insects.

The global population of Eleonora's Falcon (*Falco eleonorae*), which numbers only 5,000–8,000 pairs, breeds almost exclusively on remote sea cliffs around the Mediterranean, particularly in the Aegean, and winters in East Africa and Madagascar. This said, around 10 per cent breeds in Spanish territory, the vast majority in the Baleares, although small enclaves are also found in the Columbretes (some 30 pairs) and northern Lanzarote (about 80 pairs). Like the Lesser Kestrel, Eleonora's Falcon nests in colonies, but it differs in delaying the onset of breeding until July, with the chicks not hatching until the end of August. This timing coincides with the

appearance of the migrating passerines that make up a large part of its diet. While the females dedicate themselves almost exclusively to the care of the chicks, the males hunt in groups, positioning themselves at some height above the surface of the sea, then plunging down into the middle of small bands of migrants as they leave the shore. Outside migration periods Eleonora's Falcons feed primarily on insects.

Bustards and Sandgrouse

The vast, rolling plains of central Spain's *Meseta* harbour a significant fraction of Europe's Great and Little Bustards (family Otididae). The spring courtship display of the sexually dimorphic Great Bustard (*Otis tarda*) – the bulky males of which can weigh as much as 16 kg, with the much slighter females weighing just 3.5–5 kg – is surely one of the most memorable events in the Spanish ornithological calendar. Before mating, the highly promiscuous male Great Bustard endeavours to attract as many females as possible, to which end this essentially brown bird inflates his gular pouch into a large, pendulous balloon, tips his head back to flourish his white moustaches, and twists and fans his wings so as to expose the large white inner secondary feathers. The end result is something resembling a giant snowball, but it must do the trick, as there are currently about 23,000 Great Bustards in Spain, around half of which are found in Castilla y León.

ABOVE During the courtship display, the male Great Bustard twists and fans his wings so as to expose the large white inner secondaries.
BELOW The striking black-and-white neck markings of the male Little Bustard are present only in the breeding season.

Like the Great Bustard, the Little Bustard (*Tetrax tetrax*) is a polygamous species, and come the spring, the male dons a smart black-and-white, V-necked waistcoat and selects a territory in which to wow prospective females with a series of wing-flashing leaps and foot-stomping antics, accompanied by abrupt, snort-like calls that carry for some distance. Once mating has taken place, male bustards of both species take no further part in the reproductive process, with the incubation of the eggs and rearing of the young being the exclusive domain of the females. Both Great and Little Bustards are ground-nesting species that feed primarily on insects, so it is not surprising that intensification of agricultural practices is adversely affecting their populations in Spain and other parts of Europe. It is of particular concern that Little Bustards do not start breeding until they are six or seven years old, and yet their average lifespan in the wild rarely exceeds ten years.

The more arid pseudosteppes of the Iberian Peninsula harbour a significant proportion of Europe's two species of sandgrouse. In the case of the Pin-tailed Sandgrouse (*Pterocles alchata*), no less than 90 per cent of the European population breeds in Spain. However, although numbers were estimated

at a maximum of 22,000 birds in 1999, a 2005 census located only 8,000–11,000 birds, confined to widely dispersed localities in the Ebro Basin, the *Meseta*, Extremadura and western Andalucía. Spanish Black-bellied Sandgrouse (*P. orientalis*) populations have also declined by about 30 per cent in the last 20 years, with a maximum of 13,000 birds remaining today, of which up to 3,500 individuals occur in the Canaries, principally on Fuerteventura.

Gulls and Terns

Almost all of the 22,000 pairs of Audouin's Gull (*Larus audouinii*) in the world breed on Spain's Mediterranean coast, in the Baleares and on the Islas Chafarinas. By far the most important colony is located in the Ebro Delta, and numbered almost 14,000 pairs in 2005. Although all the major breeding colonies have been designated Special Protection Areas under European law, it is this very concentration of a large part of the global population in just a few localities that makes the species so vulnerable, particularly to predatory rats, cats and Yellow-legged Gulls (*L. michahellis*).

Spain is also home to a significant proportion of the Palaearctic population of Gull-billed Terns (*Gelochelidon nilotica*). Although breeding success fluctuates wildly from year to year according to levels of rainfall, 3,000–3,500 pairs are distributed across a dozen or so wetlands in mainland Spain, both in the interior and along the Mediterranean and southern Atlantic coasts. As is the case with many ground-nesting birds, for protection against predators Gull-billed Tern chicks are nid-

ABOVE Male Pin-tailed Sandgrouse often visit water at first light, soaking up water in their breast feathers to transport back to their chicks.
BELOW Unlike other large European *Larus* spp., Audouin's Gulls rarely scavenge but feed almost exclusively on fish.

ifugous, covered with downy feathers when they hatch and able to leave the nest within 3–4 days. Spain also holds Western Europe's foremost breeding colonies of Whiskered Terns (*Chlidonias hybridus*), numbering up to 8,000 pairs in a good year, the majority of which are located in Doñana and the Ebro Delta.

The Little Tern (*Sterna albifrons*) is another species for which Spain is one of the principal strongholds in Western Europe, most of its 5,000-odd pairs preferring to nest on the southern Atlantic coast or in the Ebro Delta. Although the species is not at grave risk in Spain as a whole, many of the inland colonies have disappeared in the last few decades, especially those that occupied the margins of major rivers that have been affected by dam construction and canalization.

Passage and Wintering Birds

Not surprisingly, mainland Spain is also of international significance for migratory birds, especially those following the so-

BELOW Tens of thousands of Common Cranes disperse in small groups across the *dehesas* of south-west Spain during the winter.

called western Mediterranean flyway. Birds heading north from Africa in the spring opt for the shortest sea crossing, entering Spain near Tarifa. They subsequently follow the eastern shores of Spain to reach their breeding grounds in Europe, stopping to rest and feed en route at the chain of coastal wetlands, for example at Mar Menor, the Albufera de València, the Marjal del Moro, the Ebro Delta and the Aiguamolls de l'Empordà; this scenario is reversed in the autumn.

Many northern European birds, however, find Spain itself an attractive winter residence, particularly wildfowl and waders, with the marshes of Doñana, for example, regularly hosting more than a million water birds at this time of year. Similarly, the Lagunas de Villafáfila (Zamora) are renowned for their winter concentrations of Greylag Geese (*Anser anser*), while the Laguna de Gallocanta, in southern Aragón, attracts up to 60,000 Common Cranes (*Grus grus*) in November and again in late February, most of which spend the intervening period feeding on acorns in south-west Spain.

Other northern European birds that do not breed in Spain but habitually choose to spend the winter in the country include Merlins (*Falco columbarius*) and Eurasian Golden Plovers (*Pluvialis apricaria*).

MAMMALS

Excluding taxa introduced in the last 100 years, more than 90 species of terrestrial mammal are known to inhabit mainland Spain, the Balearic Islands and the Canaries – testimony to the unspoiled nature of the wider countryside – with a further 9 species occurring in the North African enclaves of Ceuta and Melilla.

Due to the geographical isolation of the Iberian Peninsula and Baleares – separated from the rest of Europe by the Pyrenees and otherwise surrounded by sea – it is perhaps not surprising that six of the mammals occurring in Spain and Portugal are found nowhere else in the world. These are the Spanish Shrew (*Sorex granarius*), Iberian Mole (*Talpa occidentalis*), Cabrera's Vole (*Microtus cabrerae*), Iberian Hare (*Lepus granatensis*), Broom Hare (*L. castroviejoi*) and Iberian Lynx (*Lynx pardinus*). Moreover, although mammals are notoriously poor at colonizing remote oceanic islands, having arrived they are very likely to evolve into new species, as is evinced by the existence of two species unique to the Canary Islands archipelago, the Canary Shrew (*Crocidura canariensis*) and the Canary Big-eared Bat (*Plecotus teneriffae*).

Insectivores

Shrews, moles and hedgehogs belong to the order Insectivora, one of the oldest mammalian groups, which first appeared in the mid-Cretaceous around 135 million years ago. Spanish insectivores are all smallish creatures, the largest being the Western Hedgehog (*Erinaceus europaeus*), with a maximum body length of about 27 cm, while at the other end of the scale the Pygmy White-toothed Shrew (*Suncus etruscus*), often measuring less than 5 cm excluding the tail, is the tiniest ground-dwelling mammal in the world.

BELOW Following centuries of persecution, today Iberian Grey Wolves rarely congregate in anything larger than small family groups.

ABOVE The Greater White-toothed Shrew is one of the larger Spanish *Sorex* species, but even so it measures just 7.5–13.5 cm including the tail.

Shrews

Shrews (family Soricidae) are endearing little creatures, possessing long, mobile noses and fairly short, fur-clad tails. They are for the most part nocturnal, and although their sight is poor, they possess an excellent sense of smell and can also locate their prey – insects, arachnids, worms and molluscs – by

BELOW Algerian Hedgehogs can be distinguished from European Hedgehogs by the fact that their ears extend beyond the spines.

echolocation. The Spanish species can be separated into three principal genera: *Sorex* (four species) and *Neomys* (two species), both of which have red-tipped teeth and ears virtually concealed within their fur, and *Crocidura* (three species), distinguished by their all-white teeth and visible ears. *Sorex* and *Crocidura* species are greyish or brownish all over, while the water shrews of the genus *Neomys* are distinguished by their pure-white bellies.

Most Spanish members of the genus *Sorex* inhabit humid grasslands and forests, and are confined to mountainous areas, particularly in the north, although the predominantly central European Common Shrew (*S. araneus*) only just creeps into the country in the eastern Pyrenees. Little is known about the ecology of the Iberian endemic Spanish Shrew (*S. granarius*), but it seems to be confined to montane woodland habitats in the Sistema Central, Galicia and the northern half of Portugal, with an outlying population in the Sistema Ibérico.

The Greater White-toothed Shrew (*Crocidura russula*) is widespread throughout mainland Spain, also occurring on Ibiza, but the Lesser White-toothed Shrew (*C. suaveolens*) prefers damper habitats and is pretty well confined to the extreme northern and western seaboard of the Iberian Peninsula, particularly favouring hay meadows. Curiously, however, an endemic subspecies (*C. s. balearica*) is present on Menorca. The endemic Canary Shrew (*C. canariensis*), by contrast, ekes out a precarious existence in the lava fields of Fuerteventura and Lanzarote, with the highest population density recorded on the uninhabited – and thus cat-free – islet of Montaña Clara.

Moles and the Iberian Desman

The family Talpidae is represented by just three species in Spain: the Common Mole (*Talpa europaea*), which is widespread in Europe, the rather smaller Iberian Mole (*T. occidentalis*), found principally in the northern and western reaches of the Iberian Peninsula, but also in the Sierra Nevada, where it can reach altitudes of 2,000 m, and the Iberian Desman (*Galemys pyrenaicus*). The poor eyesight of the Common Mole became common knowledge when Kenneth Grahame wrote *The Wind in the Willows*, but its congener the Iberian Mole is even worse off: its eyes are permanently covered by a thin membrane, so it is completely blind. Both of these moles lead a mainly subterranean existence and feed almost exclusively on earthworms and insect larvae.

The Iberian or Pyrenean Desman is an unmistakable creature. Although it is essentially mole-like, its adoption of a mainly aquatic way of life has led to the development of several distinctive morphological features: a thick, waterproof coat, a flattened, trumpet-shaped nose covered with sensitive hairs, used to locate the aquatic invertebrates on which it feeds, and webbed feet and a laterally compressed tail to aid propulsion through the water. The Iberian Desman occurs only in southern France and Iberia, where it inhabits clean, well-oxygenated mountain streams in the Pyrenees, Cordillera Cantábrica, northern Portugal and the mountains of central Spain. In areas with a strong oceanic influence it can be found almost at sea level, but in more continental regions the upper limit of its range lies at around 2,500 m.

Hedgehogs

Hedgehogs (family Erinaceidae) are instantly recognizable by their thick covering of spines, estimated at more than 6,000 in the case of the Western Hedgehog (*Erinaceus europaeus*), which occurs throughout mainland Spain at altitudes of up to 1,600 m. The very similar Algerian Hedgehog (*Atelerix algirus*) is a North African species that was almost certainly introduced to Spain in ancient times as a source of food. Today it occurs all along the Spanish Mediterranean coast, in the Baleares and on the eastern and central Canaries.

Bats

Bats (order Chiroptera) are unlike any other mammals in that they have spent the last 50 million years or so adapting to an aerial existence. In the process, their fingers have become extraordinarily long so as to carry the membranes that form the wings, and their knees bend backwards rather than forwards. Bats are almost exclusively nocturnal and hunt their prey by a process known as echolocation, in which they rapidly emit high-frequency signals (inaudible to humans) through the mouth or nose. On coming into contact with a solid object, even one as small as a flying insect, these signals bounce back and are received by the bats' relatively large ears, enabling them to build up a mental picture of their immediate environs. Different genera of bats echolocate at different frequencies, and can be identified using a bat detector.

Female bats rarely produce more than one infant each year, and most do not start to breed until they are several years old, so populations increase only very slowly. More to the point, because they tend to roost and hibernate communally, whole colonies can be destroyed when ancient trees are felled or buildings are knocked down. Bats are therefore very vulnerable creatures, and all the Spanish species are protected both by the European Habitats Directive and by national legislation. Although almost a quarter of all the world's mammals are bats, just 3 families occur in Spain, represented by some 30 species.

European Free-tailed Bat

The only European member of the Molossidae is the European Free-tailed Bat (*Tadarida teniotis*), one of the largest bats in the region. It has velvety charcoal-grey fur, broad, forward-pointing ears, larger eyes than in the majority of European species and a rather thick tail that projects several centimetres beyond the tail membrane. It is found throughout mainland Spain and both archipelagos, flying in open habitats and high above towns,

ABOVE Lesser Horseshoe Bats are the smallest of the genus *Rhinolophus* in Europe, weighing just 3.5–10 g.
BELOW The dark facial mask around the eyes serves to distinguish Mehely's Horseshoe Bat from other species in the genus.

ABOVE The Greater Mouse-eared Bat is a highly gregarious species, living in colonies of hundreds, if not thousands.

where its long, narrow wings (with a wingspan of about 40 cm) can be used to the best effect, in rapid, direct flight in pursuit of large nocturnal insects such as moths and beetles.

Horseshoe Bats

Spain harbours four of the five European species of horseshoe bat (family Rhinolophidae), which are named after the semi-

BELOW Although widespread in Spain, Geoffroy's Bat is nowhere common and apparently leaves the country during the winter.

circular membrane, the noseleaf, that surrounds the nostrils and is used in echolocation. When roosting, horseshoe bats hang upside down by their toes, the infants often enfolded within the wings of the females with their heads directed upwards. Because they hunt in forested habitats, to avoid collisions with trees horseshoe bats display a slower, more erratic flight than open-country species. Their tails are relatively short, and they can be recognized in flight by the almost concave arch of the membrane between the hind legs, which is obviously convex in the longer-tailed members of the Vespertilionidae (see below).

The largest European member of the genus is the Greater Horseshoe Bat (*Rhinolophus ferrumequinum*), but even so individuals rarely weigh more than 30 g. It is found throughout the Iberian Peninsula and the Baleares, but is extinct on Ibiza. Lesser Horseshoe Bats (*R. hipposideros*) – the smallest of the genus (maximum weight 10 g) – have a similar distribution (including Ibiza), but Mediterranean Horseshoe Bats (*R. euryale*) are absent from the Balearic Islands, while Mehely's Horseshoe Bats (*R. mehelyi*) occur mainly in the lowlands of the southern half of the peninsula and Mallorca.

Vespertilionid Bats

The great majority of the Spanish bats belong to the family Vespertilionidae. Unlike the horseshoe bats, they emit echolocation signals through their open mouths, and all are very agile on the ground, crawling rapidly quadrapedally using their thumbs and hind feet. Of the nine species of *Myotis* in Spain, the most widespread in the peninsula are Geoffroy's Bat (*M. emarginatus*) and Natterer's Bat (*M. nattereri*), both of which typically inhabit forested, hilly terrain, while the Greater Mouse-eared Bat (*M. myotis*) and Lesser Mouse-eared Bat (*M. blythii*) are both gregarious species that are associated with more Mediterranean habitats, forming large colonies in underground caves.

Particularly endangered in Spain is the Long-fingered Bat (*M. capaccinii*), with fewer than 30 breeding nuclei being known from the country. It characteristically hunts over water and is strictly cavernicolous, with a distribution limited to the limestone hills along the eastern seaboard of the peninsula and on the Balearic Islands. Over Europe as a whole, however, the rarest species in the genus *Myotis* is Bechstein's Bat (*M. bechsteinii*), possibly because it is particularly associated with ancient forests, solitarily secreting itself in holes in trees for a considerable part of the year.

The pipistrelles are the smallest Spanish bats, and also some of the most widespread and abundant, particularly the Common Pipistrelle (*Pipistrellus pipistrellus*). Nathusius's Pipistrelle (*P. nathusii*) is a predominantly central European species confined to the northern and eastern seaboard of Spain, while Kuhl's and Savi's Pipistrelles (*P. kuhli* and *Hypsugo savii*) are more Mediterranean species, distributed throughout the Iberian Peninsula, Baleares and Canary Islands. The Madeira Pipistrelle (*Pipistrellus maderensis*) is a Macaronesian endemic that in Spain occurs only on the western and central Canary Islands.

All three European noctules are present in Spain, but because they prefer montane forests they have a very scattered distribution in the peninsula. The Noctule (*Nyctalus noctula*) is particularly rare, with breeding populations confirmed only in the provinces of Madrid and Navarra, while Leisler's Bat (*N. leisleri*) is the only representative of the genus on the Canaries, present on Tenerife and La Palma.

The Greater Noctule (*N. lasiopterus*) is without a doubt the most corpulent of all European bats, with the largest individuals weighing in at approximately 60 g. In recent years it has been discovered that the Greater Noctule frequently preys on migratory passerines, apparently seizing them from their night-time perches; it neatly abscises the wings of the birds before eating the rest.

Members of the genus *Plecotus* are characterized by their enormous, almost rabbit-like ears. The Grey Long-eared Bat (*P. austriacus*) is found throughout Spain and the Baleares, while the Brown Long-eared Bat (*P. auritus*) is confined to broadleaved forests above 1,000 m in the northern reaches of the Iberian Peninsula. By contrast, the Canary Big-eared Bat (*P. teneriffae*) is endemic to the Canary Islands, where it is known only from Tenerife, La Palma and El Hierro. Here the warm climate enables it to fly all year round, even at relatively high altitudes – it has been recorded at 2,300 m above sea level.

ABOVE Savi's Pipistrelle is a solitary species for much of the year, becoming gregarious only during the breeding season.
BELOW The Greater Noctule is one of the least-known mammalian species in Europe.

ABOVE Because it can tolerate long periods without water, the Algerian Mouse is the most abundant rodent of Spain's arid lands.

Rodents

Rodents (order Rodentia) are gnawing creatures with 'self-sharpening' teeth. The coating of very hard enamel on the surfaces of the teeth nearest to the lips is backed by a softer layer

BELOW Because they prefer coniferous and deciduous forests, Red Squirrels are absent from much of the *Meseta* and southern Spain.

on the side oriented towards the tongue, which wears away more rapidly. The great majority of Spanish rodents are either voles (family Arvicolidae) or rats and mice (family Muridae).

Voles

One of the most specialized members of the Arvicolidae in Spain is the Snow Vole (*Chionomys nivalis*), a pale greyish creature with prominent whiskers, confined to mountainous regions in Europe. Snow Voles are found principally in the Cordillera Cantábrica, Pyrenees and Sistema Central, with an isolated outpost in the Sierra Nevada. They tend to prefer rocky habitats high above the tree-line and are active mainly by day.

Typically Euro-Siberian species such as Water, Bank and Common Voles (*Arvicola terrestris*, *Myodes glareolus* and *Microtus arvalis*) are restricted to humid habitats in the northern reaches of Spain, while the world distribution of the quasi-endemic Pyrenean Pine Vole (*Microtus gerbei*) is restricted to montane grasslands in the eastern Pyrenees. By contrast, Cabrera's Vole (*M. cabrerae*) is associated principally with wetland vegetation in central and south-eastern Spain and southern Portugal. Nowadays it is a considered to be an Iberian endemic, although fossil evidence shows that its distribution formerly extended into southern France.

Lusitanian and Mediterranean Pine Voles (*Microtus lusitanicus* and *M. duodecimcostatus*) also display a predominantly Iberian distribution. They are thought to have become separate

species some time in the Quaternary period, and today occur in almost mutually exclusive sections of the peninsula: Lusitanian Pine Voles are surface-dwelling creatures of the humid north-western corner, while Mediterranean Pine Voles lead a primarily subterranean existence in drier habitats of the southern and eastern reaches.

Rats and Mice

Most Spanish members of the family Muridae are widespread in continental Europe, with cosmopolitan species such as Brown and Black Rats (*Rattus norvegicus* and *R. rattus*) and the Western House Mouse (*Mus domesticus*) living in close proximity to humans throughout Spain. Perhaps the only exception is the Algerian Mouse (*M. spretus*), whose European distribution is limited to rather arid habitats in mainland Iberia, the Baleares and south-eastern France.

The Harvest Mouse (*Micromys minutus*) is confined to the extreme northern reaches of Spain. It is the smallest rodent in Europe, distinguished by its reddish coat and white belly, blunt nose and prehensile tail. An agile climber, it is typically found in hay meadows, cereal fields and reed beds, where it constructs a spherical summer nest of interwoven grass blades. It usually spends the winter in an underground burrow.

Dormice

The dormice (family Gliridae) occupy an intermediate taxonomic position between mice and squirrels. The two Spanish species are the Fat or Edible Dormouse (*Glis glis*) and the Garden Dormouse (*Eliomys quercinus*), both of which are essentially nocturnal, herbivorous creatures with large eyes and ears. The Edible Dormouse, with its bushy tail, is a predominantly tree-dwelling creature, in Spain found only in mature forests in the northern Atlantic zone and Pyrenees. It lives in small groups comprising several families, but as it is extremely timid its presence often goes undetected.

The Garden Dormouse is easily distinguished by its black mask, which extends from the whiskers to behind the ear around each eye, and by its slender tail, which ends in a broad, flattened tip, rather like a paintbrush. It is less arboreal than the Edible Dormouse, often constructing nests among piles of stones, in dense scrub and even in buildings, and can be found throughout the Iberian Peninsula and Baleares.

Squirrels

The Red Squirrel (*Sciurus vulgaris*) is the only native member of the family Sciuridae in Spain, although Alpine Marmots (*Marmota marmota*) were introduced to the French Pyrenees for food in the mid-20th century, since which time they have colonized almost the whole length of the chain. Meanwhile the single pair of Barbary Ground Squirrels (*Atlantoxerus getulus*) – prolific breeders indigenous to north-west Africa – that accidentally escaped on Fuerteventura in 1965 has generated a present-day population of more than 300,000 individuals.

Although some Spanish Red Squirrels are so dark as to be almost black, they are instantly recognizable by their white-furred bellies, long, thick, bushy tails and tufted ears. They are magnificent climbers, negotiating the canopy of both deciduous and coniferous forests with consummate ease, and construct spherical nests that are known as dreys near the tops of the trees. Like dormice, Red Squirrels are largely vegetarian, feeding on a wide range of tree seeds, especially hazelnuts and pine kernels.

Rabbits and Hares

Rabbits and hares (order Lagomorpha) possess exceptionally long, mobile ears and a very short tail, as well as being designed for moving at speed, with long hind legs and a laterally flattened, streamlined body. Less apparent at first sight are their double upper incisors – a second pair lies behind the first – and their slit-like nostrils, which can be opened and closed with a fold of skin. All lagomorphs are herbivorous and practise pseudorumination, whereby food passes rapidly through the gut the first time around, to be eaten again as it leaves the anus, and thus digested twice in order to extract the maximum amount of nutrients.

BELOW The Iberian Hare is the smallest of the three Spanish *Lepus* species, weighing just 2–2.5 kg, but has the longest tail.

The pan-European Brown Hare (*Lepus europaeus*) has a north-easterly distribution in Spain, almost mutually exclusive with that of the endemic Iberian Hare (*L. granatensis*), which is by far the most common of the Spanish species. By contrast, the Broom Hare (*L. castroviejoi*) is unique to the western Cordillera Cantábrica, where it inhabits grasslands and tall scrub above the tree-line. Broom Hares can be distinguished from Iberian Hares by the distinctive white facial bands that extend from their eyes to the lower cheeks.

All three Spanish hares have black-topped tails that are held horizontally as they run, and conspicuous black tips to their very elongated ears. These features serve to distinguish them from European Rabbits (*Oryctolagus cuniculus*), which display the fluffy white undersides of their tails when running, and whose much shorter ears lack the black markings. Rabbits are almost ubiquitous across mainland Spain and both archipelagos, but their populations have crashed in recent years following a spate of disease.

Carnivores

Five families of the order Carnivora occur in mainland Spain and the Balearic Islands, represented by 15 native species. Despite the name, many members of the order are in fact omnivorous, supplementing their diet with nuts, berries and carrion when the hunting is poor. Nevertheless, all carnivores have evolved strong jaws with specialized shearing teeth and highly developed canines.

Bears

The Brown Bear (*Ursus arctos*) is the only representative of the family Ursidae to occur in temperate regions of Europe. It is by far the largest of the Spanish carnivores, with adult males weighing in at a maximum of 250 kg. Even so, Spanish Brown Bears are among the smallest members of their species in the world, veritable miniatures compared to the New World Grizzlies that sometimes tip the scales at more than 1,000 kg. Stockily built, bears have short, powerful legs, small eyes and ears, and a short tail, with a coat colour that ranges from chestnut through dark brown to almost black.

Bears – like humans – are plantigrades, meaning that the whole sole of the foot makes contact with the ground, heel first, and although this gait is not designed for acceleration, bears can reach 50 km per hour over short distances. They have poor eyesight and only average hearing, relying heavily on their sense of smell to locate food.

Although formerly widespread across the Iberian Peninsula, the Brown Bear is today confined to forested habitats in the central and eastern Pyrenees and the Cordillera Cantábrica. By the end of the 20th century only one or two native bears remained in the Spanish Pyrenees, but the population has been boosted – rightly or wrongly – by the introduction of individuals from Slovenia.

The situation of the Cantabrican bears is somewhat more stable, although the plethora of road and rail links between Oviedo and León has effectively divided the population in two. The so-called 'western nucleus', centred on Somiedo, is by far the larger, but even so was thought to comprise only 80–100 bears in 2005, while the 'eastern nucleus', straddling northern León and Palencia, is in a critical way, with just 20–25 bears remaining, so that inbreeding is a very real threat.

Brown Bears are perhaps the most herbivorous of all Spanish carnivores, especially in the autumn, when they gorge themselves on beechmast, acorns and berries in order to build up fat reserves to survive the winter. In spring, Spanish Brown Bears feed extensively on plant material, but they may consume carrion or even attack young domestic livestock or deer in early summer. Their love of honey is legendary, and they frequently raid beehives, even those that are located quite close to human habitation.

While the Spanish bears do not truly hibernate, they tend to hole up in caves for the worst of the winter. In January or February, one, two or even three tiny, almost hairless cubs are born, each weighing less than half a kilogram, but they grow rapidly, reaching 15–20 kg by the end of their first year. Male bears form no lasting family bonds and are highly promiscuous, travelling long distances every summer in order to mate with as many females as possible.

Dogs

The Red Fox (*Vulpes vulpes*) and Grey Wolf (*Canis lupus*) are the only native representatives of the family Canidae in Spain, both confined to the mainland. While the Red Fox is one of the most widespread and best-known of all European mammals, often living in close proximity to human habitation, the Grey Wolf has long been persecuted by man, so that today Spain and Portugal house the only viable populations of the species in Western Europe.

Iberian Grey Wolves are often assigned to the subspecies *C. l. signatus*, which is characterized by a black-topped tail and a blackish stripe down the front of each foreleg. They are found primarily in the north-western quadrant of the peninsula, with a relict population present in the Sierra Morena. They are very adaptable creatures, able to thrive in all manner of habitats, from thick montane forests to the cereal pseudosteppes of the *Meseta*, but without exception they are confined to areas with a low human population density.

'Packs' of wolves are definitely a thing of the past in Spain, with small family groups being the order of the day. These are usually composed of a breeding pair and its offspring, sometimes augmented by youngsters from previous years. Iberian Wolves are primarily nocturnal and have been known to cover distances of up to 50 km in a single night.

OPPOSITE The principal nuclei of Spanish Brown Bears inhabit deciduous forests and montane scrub in the Cordillera Cantábrica.

ABOVE Grey Wolves of the Iberian endemic subspecies *Canis lupus signatus* bear a black stripe down the front of each foreleg.

Spanish population estimated at about 2,000 individuals today. Although compensation is paid to farmers who have lost livestock to wolves, illegal shooting and trapping continue to take place; the Sierra Morena population is particularly at risk.

Mustelids

The family Mustelidae is represented by eight native species in Spain. All are fairly widespread across Europe, with the exception of the European Mink (*Mustela lutreola*). Following its extinction in northern and central Europe, the European Mink is nowadays an essentially eastern European species, with an outlying enclave in western France and northern Spain. The Spanish population is centred on the País Vasco, La Rioja and Navarra, where it is confined to the lower and middle reaches of unpolluted watercourses. The

In an ideal world, the Iberian Grey Wolf would prey predominantly on wild ungulates, particularly deer, but today these have often been usurped by domestic livestock. Not surprisingly, wolves are unable to distinguish between wild and domesticated animals, hence the age-old rivalry, which probably originated with Neolithic man. Nevertheless, wolves are quite capable of surviving on a diet of small mammals, birds, reptiles, amphibians and even fish. They often visit carrion and have even been known to frequent rubbish tips on the outskirts of major cities.

The Iberian Grey Wolf population suffered a major decline in the 19th and 20th centuries, but in response to milder winters in recent years, coupled with people's growing interest in the natural world, numbers have increased slightly, with the

species' diet consists mainly of fish, small mammals and birds, with crustaceans, amphibians and reptiles at certain times of the year.

As a rule, Spanish mustelids are long-bodied and short-legged. They range in size from the diminutive, slender Least Weasel (*Mustela nivalis*), one of the smallest of all carnivores, the females of which rarely weigh more than 80 g, to the relatively robust Eurasian Badger (*Meles meles*), the males of which can top 10 kg. Least Weasels, Eurasian Badgers, Western Polecats (*Mustela putorius*) and Beech Martens (*Martes foina*) occur throughout the Iberian Peninsula, but Stoats (*Mustela erminea*) and Pine Martens (*Martes martes*) are confined to the northern sector. Eurasian Otters (*Lutra lutra*) are associated mainly with rivers and marshes, but also inhabit coastal regions in Asturias, Galicia and south-western Andalucía. Only Pine Martens (subspecies *M. m. minoricensis*) and Least Weasels represent the family on the Balearic Islands.

Genets and Mongooses

The absence of fossil remains suggests that the two Spanish representatives of the family Viverridae – the Egyptian Mongoose (*Herpestes ichneumon*) and Small-spotted Genet (*Genetta genetta*) – were brought over from North Africa by the Moors in the 8th century.

The Small-spotted Genet, at least, was probably a deliberate introduction, ostensibly to rid the North Africans' dwellings of rats and mice, although this role was later taken over by the less evil-smelling domestic cat. Today the Small-spotted Genet has made itself at home in all four corners of the peninsula, and is also represented by an endemic subspecies (*G. g. isabelae*) on the Balearic island of Ibiza, where it is the only carnivore in residence and feeds principally on small lizards.

Because Small-spotted Genets are primarily nocturnal they are seldom seen, but even a glimpse in the headlights is enough to identify this distinctive animal, with its low-slung, tawny body, conspicuously spotted with black – the spots sometimes arranged in longitudinal stripes – and its bushy, black-ringed tail. Small-spotted Genets are superb climbers, using their long tails for balance, but are equally at home in treeless, rocky habitats. They prey mainly on small rodents but might also take young rabbits, supplementing their diet with berries and insects at certain times of the year.

By contrast, the strictly terrestrial Egyptian Mongoose is confined to the south-western corner of the Iberian Peninsula. It is by far the most diurnal carnivore in Spain, and can often be seen wending its way sinuously through the trees – short legs almost invisible behind the long fur of its flanks – in broad daylight. Although invertebrates, young rabbits and rodents form the major part of the Egyptian Mongoose's diet, it is not averse to taking on snakes and is reputed to be immune to their venom. In contrast to the eyes of other carnivores, those of mongooses have elongated, horizontal pupils.

Felines

Just two member of the family Felidae – the most carnivorous of all the carnivores – are known to occur in

ABOVE Small-spotted Genets are primarily nocturnal creatures, spending the daylight hours holed up in dead trees or caves.

Spain: the European Wildcat (*Felis silvestris*) and the endemic and highly threatened Iberian Lynx (*Lynx pardinus*, see also box, page 47). European Wildcats are found throughout mainland Spain except in coastal and very arid regions, but are absent from the archipelagos.

Even in the parts of Spain where European Wildcats and Iberian Lynxes overlap, there is little likelihood of confusion

BELOW Otters tend to occupy linear territories along rivers and shorelines, which they patrol on a nightly basis.

between the two species. The Iberian Lynx is a fairly hefty beast, reaching about half a metre at the shoulder, with long legs, a short, erect, black-tipped tail, black, paintbrush-like tufts of fur at the ends of the ears, and – in the adults – distinctive, pointed 'sideburns' that hang down on either side of the jaw. European Wildcats, by contrast, rather resemble domestic tabbies, but are always more robust, with a very thick and long ringed tail. Their greyish-brown coat is marked with narrow vertical stripes, while that of the Iberian Lynx is golden brown, speckled with more discrete black markings. Although Iberian Lynxes prey almost exclusively on rabbits, the European Wildcat has a much more catholic diet, feeding on small mammals, birds, reptiles, amphibians and even fish.

Artiodactyla

Four families of the order Artiodactyla – often referred to as even-toed ungulates – occur in Spain.

Wild Boar

The only Spanish representative of the family Suidae is the Wild Boar (*Sus scrofa*), which occurs in almost all habitats across the length and breadth of the Iberian Peninsula. Wild Boar are in essence rather hefty, very hairy pigs, with stout bodies, virtually no necks, large heads and relatively short legs. Both sexes are armed with four sharp, upturned tusks – modified canines that come in very handy when rooting among the forest litter for fungi and plant tubers – although these are

ABOVE European Wildcats are excellent climbers, although they prefer to hunt on the ground in the open.

OPPOSITE Among the more distinctive features of the Iberian Lynx are its spotted coat, tufted ears and pointed 'side-burns'.

BELOW The northern Spanish race of the Wild Boar – *Sus scrofa castilianus*, shown here – is larger and hairier than its southern counterpart, *baeticus*.

much better developed in the males than in the females. Wild Boar are incredibly prolific, with the females coming into season for the first time when they are about 10–11 months old and giving birth to up to 12 piglets, figures more typical of a rodent than an ungulate. This goes some way towards explaining their phenomenal abundance in Spain, despite the fervour with which they are hunted each winter.

Southern Chamois and Spanish Ibex

Although the Bovidae is the largest artiodactyl family in the world, in Spain it is represented by just two native species – the Southern Chamois (*Rupicapra pyrenaica*) and the Spanish Ibex (*Capra pyrenaica*).

The Southern Chamois can be easily identified by its slender, almost vertical, hook-shaped horns and blackish eyestripes, the latter contrasting dramatically with the pale face and neck in winter. Two distinct subspecies occur in Spain, occupying quite separate geographical areas: the *Sárrio* (subspecies *Rupicapra pyrenaica pyrenaica*) of the Pyrenees, which is particularly common in the Ordesa y Monte Perdido National Park, and the *Rebeco* (subspecies *R. p. parva*) of the Cordillera Cantábrica, which reaches maximum densities in

the Picos de Europa. The reddish-brown tail of the *Rebeco* – the smallest member of the genus – serves to distinguish it from the *Sárrio*, whose tail is black.

By contrast, the much more massive Spanish Ibex occurs principally in mountain ranges in southern and eastern Spain, where it lives at altitudes of up to 3,300 metres. Sexual dimorphism is very marked in this large mountain goat, with adult males at 80–110 kg being more than twice the size of the females. In addition, the females' short, pointed horns fade into insignificance alongside those of the males, which can measure over 75 cm in the oldest individuals. Winter coat colour also serves to tell the sexes apart. This is cinnamon coloured in the females and paler, boasting extensive black patches on the flanks and sides of the neck, in the males.

Four races of the Spanish Ibex have been recorded in the Iberian Peninsula, exhibiting distinct variation in coat colour and horn shape, although two of these are now extinct. The

ABOVE Spanish Ibex are most active in the early hours of the morning and late evening in summer, but at midday during the winter.

subspecies *Capra pyrenaica pyrenaica* (central Pyrenees) disappeared forever at the end of the 20th century (see page 30), while the subspecies *C. p. lusitanica*, from the Serra do Gerês in northern Portugal, vanished about a century earlier. Nevertheless, the remaining subspecies are not in any danger, with about 50,000 individuals split between the subspecies *C. p. victoriae* in the Sierra de Gredos and Las Batuecas, and the subspecies *C. p. hispanica*, which is widespread in the Andalucían *sierras*, as well as in the Catalan enclave of Tortosa i Beseit, behind the Ebro Delta.

Deer

Three species of deer complete the list of native Spanish artiodactyls: the Roe Deer (*Capreolus capreolus*), which is the sole

ABOVE During the autumn rut, Red Deer stags compete aggressively with each another in order to establish a hierarchy of superiority.

European member of the family Capreolidae, and Red and Fallow Deer (*Cervus elaphus* and *Dama dama*), in the Cervidae. Unlike bovids, in which both sexes sport permanent horns, only male deer – known as stags or bucks – possess antlers, and these are shed and regrown every year.

The three Spanish species can be identified according to the size and shape of their antlers. Roe Deer antlers are small and relatively unbranched, those of mature Red Deer sport a number of well-developed, upturned branches and can be over 70 cm long, and Fallow Deer antlers are broadly palmate. Size is also significant, with the diminutive Roe Deer rarely weighing more than 25 kg, while a Red Deer stag can tip the scales at 160 kg. Both Fallow and Roe Deer have white rumps, often displayed prominently when they flee from danger.

Red Deer formerly occupied the whole of the Iberian Peninsula, but by the end of the 19th century they were to be found only in the Sierra Morena, Montes de Toledo and parts of Extremadura. Following large-scale reintroductions, often with sport in mind, they are again widespread in Spain, with the population estimated at more than 300,000 individuals.

Fallow Deer have a much more discrete distribution, with native populations again being restricted to central south-west Spain by the end of the 19th century, but today occupying a series of outlying nuclei deriving from 20th-century reintroductions for hunting purposes, particularly in Doñana, the Sierra de Cazorla and the eastern Pyrenees.

Roe Deer are much more abundant to the north of the Sierra Morena, particularly in the forests of the Cordillera Cantábrica, Pyrenees, Sistema Ibérico and Sistema Central, with the Cork Oak (*Quercus suber*) forests of Los Alcornocales, in western Andalucía, harbouring an isolated population.

CETACEANS

Although there is simply not enough room here to describe the enormously varied marine life of the seas surrounding the Spanish mainland and islands, no book about Spain's wildlife would be complete without a mention of the whales and dolphins (order Cetacea) that might be spotted from the shore.

Among the most habitual marine mammals in coastal waters of peninsular Spain and the Baleares are Bottlenosed, Striped and Common Dolphins (*Tursiops truncatus*, *Stenella coeruleoalba* and *Delphinus delphis*). Equally commonplace are the much larger Sperm Whale (*Physeter catodon*), the males of which can grow to a length of 19 m, and the Fin Whale (*Balaenoptera physalus*), which can be up to 25 m in length and weigh in the region of 80 tonnes. The deep, semi-tropical waters around the Canary Islands are a veritable hotspot of cetacean diversity, in which the most abundant species are the three dolphins mentioned opposite, as well as Short-finned Pilot Whales (*Globicephala macrorhynchus*), Sperm Whales, Pygmy Sperm Whales (*Kogia breviceps*) and Cuvier's Beaked Whales (*Ziphius cavirostris*).

Overall, more than 30 cetacean species have been cited from Spanish waters, pertaining to seven distinct families.

BELOW Striped Dolphins are the most abundant cetaceans in Spanish waters, particularly beyond the continental shelf.

Chapter 3

NATURE CONSERVATION IN SPAIN

Because Spain is one of the least developed countries in Western Europe, with a relatively low population density, it still harbours a wealth of fabulously scenic landscapes, rich in flora and fauna. Many of these have been protected by law so as to ensure their preservation for future generations, with particular attention being paid to the country's highly significant mountain ranges and wetlands. The vast majority of Spain's protected areas are not in state ownership, so their declaration has involved a considerable degree of cooperation between government bodies and private individuals. The Spanish public as a whole, particularly that hailing from urban areas, spends a considerable amount of leisure time exploring its natural heritage, and is well catered for in the range of interpretative facilities on offer.
In addition, the millions of foreign tourists that visit Spain each year are tending to move away from the classic 'sun and sea' holiday, instead revelling in the exceptional habitats and wildlife that the country has to offer.

LEFT The Circo de Cinco Lagunas is secreted among the glaciated heights of the Sierra de Gredos, in the Sistema Central.

National Legislation

Spain was one of the first European countries to take the protection of its natural heritage seriously, starting with the declaration of two national parks back in 1918: Ordesa y Monte Perdido, in the Aragonese Pyrenees, and the Montaña de Covadonga, which was expanded in 1995 to include all three massifs of the Picos de Europa. There then followed almost 60 years of relative stagnation – much of which can be attributed to the Civil War and Franco's authoritarian regime – relieved only by the creation of half a dozen national parks, three of which are located on the Canary Islands. During this period, the principal conservation designations elsewhere in Spain revolved around the declaration of 46 enormous *reservas nacionales de caza* (national hunting reserves), particularly in remote mountain areas, covering more than 15,000 sq km.

The death of Franco in 1975 led to the return of the monarchy and the passing of the new Constitution in December 1978. At this time, 17 autonomous communities were created, but it was not until the 1989 *Ley de Conservación de Espacios Naturales y de la Flora y Fauna* that responsibility for nature conservation was passed wholesale from central government to the regions. Although the national parks remained under state control, a whole rash of new protected areas was subsequently declared by regional governments keen to assert themselves. For many years, however, the lack of resources meant that these were largely 'paper designations'. Despite the fact that the 1989 law established four main types of protected area

BELOW Over millennia, the rivers of the Ordesa National Park have carved profound gorges through the limestone.

BELOW Proof of continuing volcanic activity in the Timanfaya National Park attracts many visitors.

– parks (both national and natural), natural reserves, natural monuments and protected landscapes – it seemed that no two of Spain's highly idiosyncratic regions could agree as to the precise classification. Today, more than a dozen categories of protected area exist in Spain, defined by regional legislation.

At about the same time, the *Ley de Costas* came into force, specifying obligations for the protection of the marine environment up to 100 m offshore, and declaring a belt 100 m wide above the high-tide mark as *dominio público*, thus proscribing coastal development. More recently, the 2007 *Ley del Patrimonio Natural y de la Biodiversidad* stipulated a complete inventory of species and natural habitats present in Spanish territory, laying the onus of preserving the country's biodiversity for future generations squarely at the door of the state and regional governments. To date, Red Data Books and comprehensive atlases have been published for continental (freshwater) fish, amphibians, reptiles, breeding birds and mammals, as well as for threatened invertebrates and vascular plants. The commitment to preserving Spain's natural habitats, flora and fauna has thus been gathering impetus for several decades, so that today the network of protected areas is vast. There is a heavy emphasis on public enjoyment and education, with the provision of information centres and interpretative guides given priority. That said, where species or habitats are considered to be particularly vulnerable to disturbance, public access is either forbidden or the numbers of visitors is strictly limited, as is the case in a number of the national parks.

Over the past 30 years, several new national parks have been added to the list, so that almost all of Spain's major habitat types are now represented in this network. The most recent addition was Monfragüe in 2007, bringing the total to 14,

BELOW Hidden coves like the Cala L'Olló abound in the Cabrera National Park (Baleares).

ABOVE The Natura 2000 site of La Serena, in southern Extremadura, is one of the most important areas for steppe birds in Spain.

which together encompass almost 3,500 sq km. Since 2006, however, responsibility for the management of these national parks is gradually being transferred to the governments of the autonomous regions in which they are located.

International Legislation

Spain has ratified a number of international conventions relating to nature conservation over the years, notably that dealing with Wetlands of International Importance Especially as Wildfowl Habitat, which was convened at Ramsar, Iran, in 1971. Today Spain has declared 63 so-called Ramsar Sites, totalling more than 2,800 sq km. The majority of these are found on the mainland, with two sites on the Baleares and one on Fuerteventura.

Spain is also a firm adherent of the UNESCO Man and the Biosphere programme, with the regions literally falling over themselves to propose so-called Biosphere Reserves. The national total currently stands at 38, some of which encompass entire islands – for example Menorca in the Baleares and La Palma, El Hierro and Lanzarote in the Canary Islands – while a massive composite site known as Gran Cantábrica embraces nine individual Biosphere Reserves and covers virtually the

whole western end of the Cordillera Cantábrica, extending as far east as the Picos de Europa.

When Spain joined the European Union – then the European Economic Community – in 1986, it was obliged to identify a series of Special Protected Areas (SPAs) under the Wild Birds Directive (79/409/EEC). By March 2008, 562 such areas had been declared in Spain, covering almost 100,000 sq km of terrestial and marine habitats and representing approximately one-fifth of the country.

In 1992, the Habitats Directive (92/43/EEC) laid a further onus on member states: to propose a national list of areas suitable for the designation of a European network of Sites of Community Importance, known as Natura 2000, in order to safeguard the biodiversity of the continent. Although in many cases these coincide with the SPAs already identified, by August 2007 Spain had proposed 1,434 Natura 2000 sites, encompassing almost 125,000 sq km (more than 23 per cent of Spain's total land area).

Non-governmental Organizations

Although in many Western European countries the voluntary sector is actively involved in the purchase of land in order to protect its habitats and species, this is not the case in Spain, firstly because there is just so much wilderness left in Spain, and secondly because the public sector is doing such an excel-

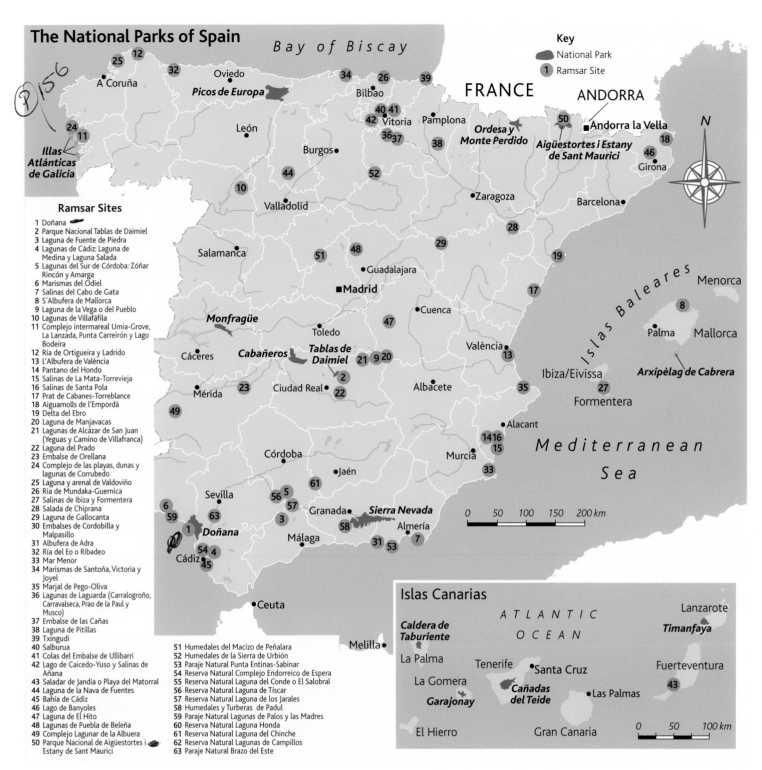

The National Parks of Spain

Bay of Biscay

FRANCE

ANDORRA

Key
- National Park
- 1 Ramsar Site

Picos de Europa

Illas Atlánticas de Galicia

Ordesa y Monte Perdido

Aigüestortes i Estany de Sant Maurici

Oviedo
A Coruña
León
Bilbao
Vitoria
Pamplona
Burgos
Andorra la Vella
Girona
Barcelona
Zaragoza
Valladolid

N

Monfragüe
Cabañeros
Tablas de Daimiel

Salamanca
Guadalajara
Madrid
Cuenca
Toledo
València
Cáceres
Ciudad Real
Albacete
Mérida
Ibiza/Eivissa
Córdoba
Jaén
Granada
Murcia
Alacant
Málaga
Almería
Sevilla
Cádiz
Ceuta
Melilla

Islas Baleares

Menorca
Palma
Mallorca
Arxipèlag de Cabrera
Formentera

Mediterranean Sea

Doñana
Sierra Nevada

0   50   100   150   200 km

Ramsar Sites

1 Doñana
2 Parque Nacional Tablas de Daimiel
3 Laguna de Fuente de Piedra
4 Lagunas de Cádiz: Laguna de Medina y Laguna Salada
5 Lagunas del Sur de Córdoba: Zóñar Rincón y Amarga
6 Marismas del Odiel
7 Salinas del Cabo de Gata
8 S'Albufera de Mallorca
9 Laguna de la Vega o del Pueblo
10 Lagunas de Villafáfila
11 Complejo intermareal Umia-Grove, La Lanzada, Punta Carreirón y Lago Bodeira
12 Ría de Ortigueira y Ladrido
13 L'Albufera de València
14 Pantano del Hondo
15 Salinas de La Mata-Torrevieja
16 Salinas de Santa Pola
17 Prat de Cabanes-Torreblance
18 Aiguamolls de l'Empordà
19 Delta de l'Ebro
20 Laguna de Manjavacas
21 Lagunas de Alcázar de San Juan (Yeguas y Camino de Villafranca)
22 Laguna del Prado
23 Embalse de Orellana
24 Complejo de las playas, dunas y lagunas de Corrubedo
25 Laguna y arenal de Valdoviño
26 Ria de Mundaka-Guernica
27 Salinas de Ibiza y Formentera
28 Salada de Chiprana
29 Laguna de Gallocanta
30 Embalses de Cordobilla y Malpasillo
31 Albufera de Adra
32 Ría del Eo o Ribadeo
33 Mar Menor
34 Marismas de Santoña, Victoria y Joyel
35 Marjal de Pego-Oliva
36 Lagunas de Laguarda (Carralogroño, Carravalseca, Prao de la Paul y Musco)
37 Embalse de las Cañas
38 Laguna de Pitillas
39 Txingudi
40 Salburua
41 Colas del Embalse de Ullibarri
42 Lago de Caicedo-Yuso y Salinas de Añana
43 Saladar de Jandía o Playa del Matorral
44 Laguna de la Nava de Fuentes
45 Bahía de Cádiz
46 Lago de Banyoles
47 Laguna de El Hito
48 Lagunas de Puebla de Beleña
49 Complejo Lagunar de la Albuera
50 Parque Nacional de Aigüestortes i Estany de Sant Maurici

51 Humedales del Macizo de Peñalara
52 Humedales de la Sierra de Urbión
53 Paraje Natural Punta Entinas-Sabinar
54 Reserva Natural Complejo Endorreico de Espera
55 Reserva Natural Laguna del Conde o El Salobral
56 Reserva Natural Laguna de Tíscar
57 Reserva Natural Laguna de los Jarales
58 Humedales y Turberas de Padul
59 Paraje Natural Lagunas de Palos y las Madres
60 Reserva Natural Laguna Honda
61 Reserva Natural Laguna del Chinche
62 Reserva Natural Lagunas de Campillos
63 Paraje Natural Brazo del Este

Islas Canarias

ATLANTIC OCEAN

Caldera de Taburiente
Lanzarote
Timanfaya
La Palma
Tenerife
Santa Cruz
Fuerteventura
La Gomera
Cañadas del Teide
Las Palmas
Garajonay
El Hierro
Gran Canaria

0   50   100 km

lent job. The principal conservation charity is the *Sociedad Española de Ornitología* (SEO), which owns and manages just six small reserves.

The SEO's associates tend to be members of the scientific community rather than the public at large, since there is no incentive to purchase membership in order to gain free access to a network of fabulous nature reserves. It is perhaps not surprising, therefore, that the SEO has just 10,000 members, a pitifully small number when compared to the million or so affiliated to the equivalent organization in the United Kingdom, the Royal Society for the Protection of Birds (RSPB). The SEO dedicates its efforts principally to investigating the Spanish avifauna, and conducting nationwide censuses of both breeding and wintering birds. That said, like most Spanish conservation organizations it is also a very political animal, much involved in lobbying the powers that be and denouncing the Spanish government to higher authorities in Europe with, it must be said, a considerable degree of success.

The other high-profile Non-governmental Organization involved with nature conservation nationally is WWF-Adena (*Asociación para la Defensa de la Naturaleza*). Additionally, almost every autonomous community can count on a small society of concerned individuals who are prepared to fight for the protection of their region's natural heritage.

Chapter 4

TOP WILDLIFE-WATCHING LOCATIONS

As a result of Spain's commitment to nature conservation, especially at a regional level, the visiting naturalist is spoilt for choice. Apart from the statutory protected areas, some key examples of which are described in the following pages, the wider countryside beyond the boundaries of these wildlife refuges also offers almost limitless opportunities for communing with nature, generally without the crowds that are attracted to the more popular destinations.

LEFT The Río Voltoya winds through granite rock outcrops and Western Holm Oaks in the Sierra de Ávila.

THE FOLLOWING IS A SELECTION of Spain's most emblematic wildlife refuges, with examples taken from all the major habitat types present in the country, both on the mainland and in the Balearic and Canary archipelagos.

1. Illas Atlánticas de Galicia National Park This 8,480-ha park encompasses a rash of small islets, notably the Illas Cíes, Ons, Sálvora and Cortegada, and their surrounding marine habitats off the west coast of Galicia. The impressive sea cliffs – which are all that remains of an ancient granitic ridge submerged during tectonic upheavals – harbour important colonies of breeding seabirds, particularly the Common Murre (*Uria aalge*), while the adjacent seas are incredibly rich in Atlantic inshore marine life.

BELOW The rugged granite coast of the Illas Cíes, in the Illas Atlánticas de Galicia National Park.

2. Corrubedo One of Spain's best-preserved Atlantic sand-dunes systems stretches for almost 4 km along the western edge of the Serra de Barbanza. All the natural elements of the dune succession occur here, from embryo dunes behind the strand-line to the tertiary dunes furthest from the sea, which host an exceptionally diverse flora. Coastal lagoons within the 996-ha *parque natural* attract many water birds on passage and during the winter, while the site as a whole is rich in Iberian endemic herptiles.

3. Somiedo Situated on the northern flanks of the Cordillera Cantábrica in Asturias, Somiedo is a dramatic montane wilderness area, 29,121 ha of which is a *parque natural* and Biosphere Reserve. Glaciated valleys clothed in thick deciduous forests and meadows give way to subalpine pastures and limestone outcrops at 2,100 m. Somiedo harbours one of the highest densities of Brown Bears (*Ursus arctos*) in Western Europe, as well as substantial populations of Black Woodpeckers (*Dryocopus martius*) and the endangered Cantabrican race of Capercaillie (*Tetrao urogallus cantabricus*).

4. Picos de Europa National Park These spectacular limestone massifs cover 64,660 ha at the junction of Asturias, Cantabria and León, peaking at 2,648 m. More than 1,500 species of vascular plant have been recorded here, ranging from a diverse high-altitude flora to traditionally managed hay meadows considered to be among the richest Atlantic grasslands in the world, teeming with orchids. The butterfly fauna is simply stupendous, with more than 150 species cited from in and around the park, while the peaks harbour the highest density of Cantabrican Southern Chamois (*Rupicapra pyrenaica parva*) in the world.

5. Marismas de Santoña A *reserva natural* and Ramsar Site (3,866 ha), this extensive coastal wetland lies at the mouth of the Río Asón in eastern Cantabria. It encompasses diverse estuarine salt marshes, freshwater reed beds, sand dunes and sea cliffs, and is important for wintering congregations of water birds. Hundreds of Eurasian Spoonbills (*Platalea leucorodia*) drop in during the autumn migration period.

6. Izki Lying on the southern flank of the Cordillera Cantábrica, in the Basque province of Araba (Álava), this vast Pyrenean Oak (*Quercus pyrenaica*) forest occupies sandy soils in the Izki river basin and is home to the highest density of Middle Spotted Woodpeckers (*Dendrocopos medius*) in the Iberian Peninsula. Peat bogs in this

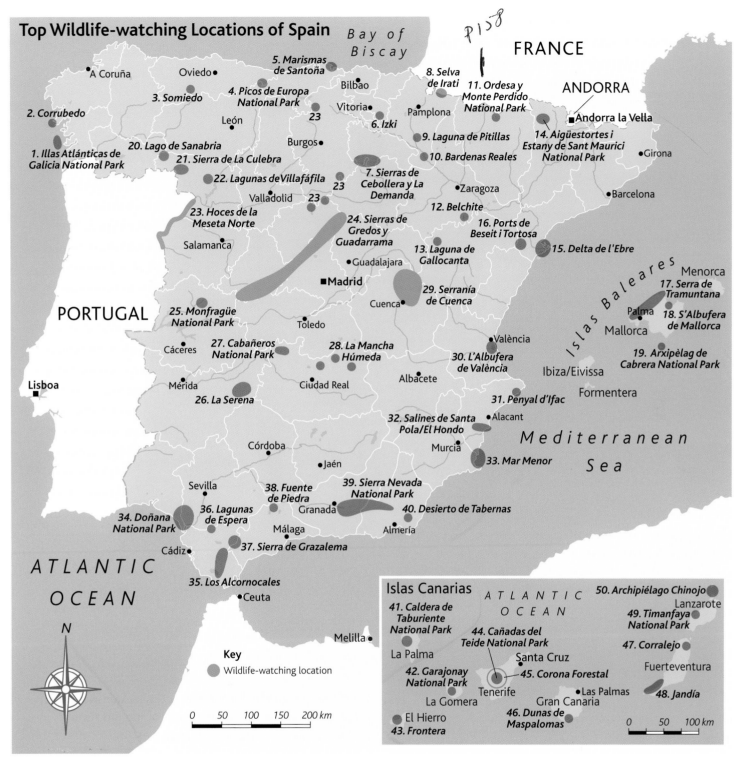

Top Wildlife-watching Locations of Spain

Bay of Biscay

FRANCE

ANDORRA

■Andorra la Vella

•A Coruña
•Oviedo

5. Marismas de Santoña

8. Selva de Irati

11. Ordesa y Monte Perdido National Park

3. Somiedo

4. Picos de Europa National Park

Bilbao

•Vitoria

2. Corrubedo

León•

23

6. Izki

Pamplona

14. Aigüestortes i Estany de Sant Maurici National Park

•Girona

1. Illas Atlánticas de Galicia National Park

20. Lago de Sanabria

Burgos•

9. Laguna de Pitillas

21. Sierra de La Culebra

23

10. Bardenas Reales

•Barcelona

22. Lagunas de Villafáfila

23

7. Sierras de Cebollera y La Demanda

•Zaragoza

Valladolid•

Islas Baleares

Menorca

23. Hoces de la Meseta Norte

23

12. Belchite

16. Ports de Beseit i Tortosa

17. Serra de Tramuntana

Salamanca•

24. Sierras de Gredos y Guadarrama

13. Laguna de Gallocanta

15. Delta de l'Ebre

Palma

18. S'Albufera de Mallorca

PORTUGAL

•Guadalajara

Mallorca

■Madrid

29. Serranía de Cuenca

19. Arxipèlag de Cabrera National Park

25. Monfragüe National Park

Cuenca•

València•

Ibiza/Eivissa

Toledo•

30. L'Albufera de València

Cáceres•

27. Cabañeros National Park

28. La Mancha Húmeda

Formentera

Lisboa

Mérida•

Albacete•

31. Penyal d'Ifac

26. La Serena

Ciudad Real•

32. Salines de Santa Pola/El Hondo

•Alacant

Mediterranean Sea

Córdoba•

Murcia•

•Jaén

33. Mar Menor

Sevilla•

38. Fuente de Piedra

39. Sierra Nevada National Park

34. Doñana National Park

36. Lagunas de Espera

Granada•

40. Desierto de Tabernas

Málaga•

Almería•

37. Sierra de Grazalema

Cádiz•

ATLANTIC OCEAN

35. Los Alcornocales

•Ceuta

Melilla•

N

Islas Canarias

ATLANTIC OCEAN

50. Archipiélago Chinojo

41. Caldera de Taburiente National Park

Lanzarote

49. Timanfaya National Park

44. Cañadas del Teide National Park

47. Corralejo

La Palma

Santa Cruz

45. Corona Forestal

Fuerteventura

42. Garajonay National Park

Tenerife

•Las Palmas

48. Jandía

La Gomera

Gran Canaria

•El Hierro

46. Dunas de Maspalomas

43. Frontera

Key
● Wildlife-watching location

0   50   100   150   200 km

0   50   100 km

---

parke naturala (9,413 ha) are renowned for their diverse communities of insectivorous plants.

7. Sierras de Cebollera y La Demanda These siliceous massifs are one of the best-preserved sectors of the Sistema Ibérico, rising to more than 2,000 m in La Rioja. Forests of European Beech (*Fagus sylvatica*) and Scots Pine (*Pinus sylvestris*) at lower levels give way to subalpine pastures dotted with glacial lakes and peat bogs. Many Euro-Siberian animals and plants reach their southernmost limits in Iberia here, with European Wildcats (*Felis silvestris*) being particularly common. The Cebollera *parque natural* covers 23,640 ha.

8. Selva de Irati Abutting the French border in northern Navarra, this immense mixed forest of European Silver-fir (*Abies alba*) and European Beech covers roughly 6,500 ha. It is home to about 60 per cent of Spain's White-backed Woodpeckers (*Dendrocopos leucotos*), with the dense network of streams harbouring the highest density of Eurasian Otters (*Lutra lutra*) in Navarra. The intense shade favours a wide range of saprophytic and parasitic vascular plants and fungi.

9. Laguna de Pitillas The most important wetland in Navarra, this *reserva natural* and Ramsar Site of 216 ha is nowadays a permanent lagoon, the margins of which harbour one of

ABOVE Autumn colours in the mixed coniferous and deciduous forest of the Ordesa National Park.

11. Ordesa y Monte Perdido National Park Some of Spain's most stunning limestone mountain scenery can be found in this, Spain's oldest national park, declared in 1918 and covering 15,608 ha in northern Aragón. Also a Biosphere Reserve, the park is rich in emblematic Pyrenean animals and plants. Among the highlights are Lammergeiers (*Gypaetus barbatus*), Rock Ptarmigans (*Lagopus mutus pyrenaicus*), Tengmalm's Owls (*Aegolius funereus*) and 130-odd species of butterfly.

12. Belchite This vast arid, stony plain to the south of Zaragoza is populated by characteristic gypsophilous and halophytic plant communities and supports a rich assemblage of steppe birds, particularly within the reserves of El Planerón and La Lomaza, the latter being possibly the best place in Spain to track down Dupont's Lark.

13. Laguna de Gallocanta Spain's largest natural inland water body – and one of the most extensive salt lakes in Western Europe – this 1,330-ha endorheic lagoon is located near Calamocha. Lying within a Ramsar Site and a *refugio de fauna silvestre* of 6,720 ha, it attracts many wintering and passage water birds, but is of greatest significance for its spring and autumn concentrations of Common Cranes (*Grus grus*): some 60,000 individuals at a time in the wettest years.

14. Aigüestortes i Estany de Sant Maurici National Park This vast, rugged granitic mountain wilderness in the Catalan Pyrenees is home to a rich Euro-Siberian and alpine flora and fauna. The 14,119-ha park – also a Ramsar Site – encompasses more than 200 glacial lakes (*estanys*) dotted among twisting mountain streams (the so-called *aigüestortes*). Among the most notable animal inhabitants are the Iberian Desman (*Galemys pyrenaica*) in the watercourses, Pyrenean Southern Chamois (*Rupicapra pyrenaica pyrenaica*) in the high pastures, and the Pyrenean subspecies of Capercaillie (*Tetrao urogallus aquitanicus*), Tengmalm's Owl and Black Woodpecker in the thick conifer forests.

15. Delta de l'Ebre The enormous arrow-shaped delta that juts into the Mediterranean at the southern end of the Catalan coast is partly a *parc natural* and Ramsar Site (7,736 ha). Its mosaic

Spain's best breeding assemblages of reed-bed birds, as well as attracting spectacular numbers of water birds during migration periods. Bustards, sandgrouse, larks and Montagu's Harriers (*Circus pygargus*) nest in the surrounding pseudosteppes.

10. Bardenas Reales A surreal landscape of eroded gypsum pinnacles emerging from a mosaic of *garrigue* and low-intensity cereal cultivations surrounding a military bombing range, this *parque natural* and Biosphere Reserve in southern Navarra covers 41,840 ha and is home to a diverse assemblage of steppe birds and cliff-breeding raptors. It is particularly noted for its 400-odd pairs of Dupont's Larks (*Chersophilus duponti*).

of rice paddies, salt marshes, coastal lagoons and sand dunes together forms a paradise for birds, harbouring nine breeding species of heron and the world's largest colony of Audouin's Gull (*Larus audouinii*). Hoards of waders and wildfowl descend on the marshes during passage periods, many of which stay for the winter.

16. Ports de Beseit i Tortosa Located just inland of the Ebro Delta, these rugged limestone massifs represent the easternmost extremity of the Sistema Ibérico, where animals and plants typical of more northerly climes find themselves cheek by jowl with species more characteristic of dry Mediterranean habitats. The high point of the *parc natural* (35,050 ha) lies 1,442 m above sea level, commanding fabulous views over the coastal plain.

17. Serra de Tramuntana Perhaps the last true wilderness area in the Baleares, this labyrinthine limestone ridge extends for some 80 km along the northern edge of Mallorca, peaking at 1,445 m. More than 30 species of vascular plant are unique to its subalpine habitats, with the Mediterranean scrub home to the endemic Balearic Warbler (*Sylvia balearica*). Sheer north-facing cliffs, in places more than 300 m high, plunge almost vertically into the sea and host important colonies of seabirds. They are dissected by gorges that harbour the bulk of the world population of the Mallorcan Midwife Toad (*Alytes muletensis*).

18. S'Albufera de Mallorca This is undoubtedly the most important coastal wetland in the Balearic archipelago, domi-

ABOVE The profound, tranquil waters of the Lago de Sanabria, fed by icy mountain streams originating in the Sierra Segundera.

nated by an enormous expanse of reed beds within which are secreted shallow lagoons and saltpans. A *parc natural* and Ramsar Site covering 1,708 ha, the primary wildlife interest is undoubtedly ornithological. Of the 230 birds cited here, more than 60 breed, notably the largest population of Moustached Warblers (*Acrocephalus melanopogon*) in the Western Mediterranean. The freshwater habitats are renowned for their diverse assemblage of dragonflies and damselflies.

19. Arxipèlag de Cabrera National Park The 20 or so islands that make up the Cabrera archipelago lie just 10 km off the southern tip of Mallorca. They are home to many Balearic endemic plants and invertebrates, Lilford's Wall Lizards and exceptional seabird colonies, with the Balearic Shearwater (*Puffinus mauretanicus*) of particular note. Of the more than 10,000 ha that comprise the national park, just 1,318 ha are terrestial, the remainder representing one of the most pristine and species-rich marine habitats in the Mediterranean. Its undersea meadows of *Posidonia oceanica* and rocky platforms harbour more than 200 species of fish.

ABOVE
20. Lago de Sanabria At 368 ha, Sanabria is the largest glacial lake in the Iberian Peninsula, more than 50 m deep in places. The *parque natural* covers 22,365 ha of high-level granite plateau in the Sierra Segundera, in Zamora, dotted with myri-

ABOVE The fabulous river canyon of the Arribes del Duero contains important populations of cliff-breeding birds.

ad smaller glacial lakes and peat bogs. Outstanding aquatic plant communities occur here, plus a unique assemblage of Euro-Siberian, Mediterranean and Iberian endemic reptiles and amphibians, notably Bosca's Newt (*Lissotriton boscai*) and Schreiber's Green Lizard (*Lacerta schreiberi*).

21. Sierra de La Culebra Extending over a vast 65,891 ha, this sparsely inhabited *espacio natural* in north-western Zamora is home to Western Europe's largest population of Grey Wolves (*Canis lupus*), despite the fact that the original deciduous forests of the range have been largely converted to conifer plantations and secondary scrub communities. The European Wildcat, Beech Marten (*Martes foina*) and Small-spotted Genet (*Genetta genetta*) are also present in good numbers.

22. Lagunas de Villafáfila These three shallow seasonal lagoons covering a maximum of 600 ha in wet winters are set among ironing board-flat arable pseudosteppes that harbour one of the highest densities of Great Bustards (*Otis tarda*) in the world,

plus notable breeding colonies of Lesser Kestrels (*Falco naumanni*). Tens of thousands of wintering waterfowl frequent the lagoon, with avian diversity increasing dramatically during passage periods. In total the *reserva natural* extends over 32,600 ha, of which the Ramsar Site comprises 2,854 ha.

23. Hoces de la Meseta Norte Over millennia, rivers traversing the high limestone plateaux of northern Castile – both the Ebro en route to the Mediterranean and tributaries of the Duero heading west to the Atlantic – have carved out a series of precipitous canyons known locally as *hoces*. Most harbour huge colonies of Griffon Vultures (*Gyps fulvus*), as well as many other cliff-breeding raptors, including the Eurasian Eagle Owl (*Bubo bubo*), and gorge-dwelling passerines. Well worth a visit are the **Hoces del Río Riaza** in Segovia, home to the largest concentration of Griffons in Iberia (390 pairs in 2000), as well as the **Hoces del Duratón**, also in Segovia, the **Cañón del Rio Lobos** straddling the Soria–Burgos boundary, and the **Hoces del Alto Ebro y Rudrón** in Burgos. Further west, where the granite and quartzite **Arribes del Duero** define the border between Spain and Portugal, Black Storks (*Ciconia nigra*) join the cliff-breeding bird assemblage.

24. Sierras de Gredos y Guadarrama
Together, these east–west-oriented, granitic mountain ranges make up the bulk of the Sistema Central, peaking at 2,592 m; they are sometimes referred to as the 'backbone of Spain'. Mediterranean evergreen forest that is located on the lowest, south-facing slopes grades into the best-preserved natural Scots Pine woods in Spain, and thence into upland scrub and granitic rock gardens above the tree-line, dotted with glacial lakes and harbouring a wide variety of endemic plants. Spanish Ibex (*Capra pyrenaica victoriae*) abound at the very highest levels, while the forests host important breeding enclaves of both the Cinereous Vulture (*Aegypius monachus*) and Spanish Imperial Eagle (*Aquila adalberti*).

25. Monfragüe National Park First protected as a *parque natural* in 1979 and upgraded to national park status in 2007, Monfragüe has long been the flagship of nature conservation in Extremadura. Its 18,118-ha mosaic of *dehesas*, primeval Mediterranean forest and quartzite ridges harbours one of the best assemblages of breeding raptors in Europe, as well as 30-odd pairs of Black Stork and many typical Mediterranean birds and forest mammals. The Tajo and Tiétar Rivers host both Common and Stripeless Tree Frogs (*Hyla arborea* and *H. meridionalis*), and both European Pond and Spanish Terrapins (*Emys orbicularis* and *Mauremys leprosa*).

26. La Serena A vast, virtually treeless expanse of dry cereal fields and pastures in eastern Extremadura, La Serena holds one of the richest steppe bird communities in Iberia, home to myriad bustards, sandgrouse and harriers. Several thousand majestic Common Cranes forage for acorns and invertebrates in the *dehesas* to the south of the nearby Sierras de Castuera y Tiros in winter.

27. Cabañeros National Park Much like Monfragüe, this 40,856-ha park in western Castilla–La Mancha is a microcosm of all the characteristic Mediterranean habitats of western

ABOVE The northern flanks of the Sierra de Guadarrama harbour Spain's most extensive Scots Pine forests.

Iberia, and is sometimes known as the 'Spanish Serengeti' on account of its diverse vertebrate fauna. Spanish Imperial Eagles, Cinereous Vultures, Black Storks and Red Deer (*Cervus elaphus*) are particularly abundant in forested habitats, while a rich community of steppe birds inhabits the extensive open grasslands, here known as *rañas*.

ABOVE The endorheic Laguna de Fuente de Piedra is the largest natural inland water body in Andalucía.

28. La Mancha Húmeda This Biosphere Reserve of around 2,500 ha encompasses three important wetland enclaves in Ciudad Real. These are the **Tablas de Daimiel National Park** (also a Ramsar Site) on the floodplain around the confluence of the Guadiana and Gigüela Rivers, where sheets of surface water – the *tablas* – harbour essentially freshwater plant communities; the shallow, endorheic **Lagunas de Alcázar de San Juan**, with their halophytic vegetation; and the unique karstic lakes of the **Lagunas de Ruidera** *parque natural*. All three of these sites are of supreme significance for nesting, passage and wintering water birds, as well as for their amphibian and odonate assemblages.

29. Serranía de Cuenca Located at the eastern edge of Castilla–La Mancha, this vast limestone upland is clothed for the most part in extensive *Pinus nigra* ssp. *salzmannii* forests, home to Spanish Moon Moths (*Graellsia isabelae*) and a good range of both Mediterranean and more typically Euro-Siberian forest birds. Exposed crags and deeply incised gorges host cliff-breeding raptors and an interesting array of endemic fissure plants. The area as a whole is renowned for its rich butterfly fauna, with highlights including the Spanish endemic Zapater's Ringlet (*Erebia zapateri*) and an isolated population of the Sandy Grizzled Skipper (*Pyrgus cinarae*).

30. L'Albufera de València Spain's third most important wetland for wintering water birds, this shallow coastal lagoon lies just south of the city of València. A *parc natural* and Ramsar Site of 21,120 ha, it is the best remaining example of the rosary of wetlands that once stretched right along the Mediterranean seaboard. Reed beds harbour an important assemblage of breeding herons, warblers and Bearded Reedlings (*Panurus biarmicus*), with more than 4,000 pairs of terns nesting in the restricted-access *reserva integral*.

31. Penyal d'Ifac This iconic block of limestone rises almost vertically from the sea not far north of Benidorm. Peaking at 332 m, the diminutive *parc natural* (45 ha) hosts a rich community of fissure plants, many of which are unique to Spain. An interesting assemblage of reptiles includes the Spanish Psammodromus (*Psammodromus hispanicus*) and both Turkish and Moorish Geckos (*Hemidactylus turcicus* and *Tarentola mauritanica*).

32. Salines de Santa Pola and El Hondo An interesting array of halophytic plants grows around the margins of the saltpans of **Santa Pola**, including locally endemic sea-lavenders. Greater

Flamingoes (*Phoenicopterus roseus*) can be seen feeding in the *salines* all year round, although they have not yet bred successfully. Myriad waders feed in the shallows, while gulls and terns fish in the deeper pools, and Collared Pratincoles (*Glareola pratincola*) hawk for insects in the airspace above. The adjacent freshwater reservoirs of **El Hondo**, fringed by thick marginal vegetation, are home to typical reed-bed birds and wildfowl, including a large percentage of Europe's breeding population of Marbled Teal (*Marmaronetta angustirostris*). Both sites have *parc natural* and Ramsar status, and are located just south of Elx/Elche.

33. Mar Menor An enormous coastal lagoon to the east of Cartagena in Murcia, separated from the Mediterranean by a 24-km sandspit, this Ramsar Site covers almost 15,000 ha and encompasses the whole gamut of lowland coastal habitats: sand dunes, saltpans, salt marshes and rocky volcanic islets. Long-fingered Bats (*Myotis capaccinii*) are commonly seen hunting over the water, while Lesser Short-toed Larks (*Calandrella rufescens*), Kentish Plovers (*Charadrius alexandrinus*) and Little Terns (*Sterna albifrons*) breed in sandy habitats.

34. Doñana National Park The showpiece of Spanish nature conservation since the 1950s, the Marismas del Guadalquivir on the Atlantic coast of south-west Spain are of exceptional ornithological significance, with more than a million birds using the marshes over the course of the year. In total more than 112,000 ha of rainwater-fed marshes and lagoons, sand dunes, saltpans and enclaves of Mediterranean forest are protected by National Park, *parque natural* and Ramsar status. In total, 378 species of bird have been recorded here, of which 136 breed regularly. They include a dozen pairs of Spanish Imperial Eagles, Europe's largest colony of Eurasian Spoonbills, more than 5,000 pairs of Purple Swamp-hens (*Porphyrio porphyrio*) and the Glossy Ibises (*Plegadis falcinellus*). The relict enclave of the endangered Iberian Lynx (*Lynx pardinus*) is the highlight among the mammals.

35. Los Alcornocales The largest Cork Oak (*Quercus suber*) forest in the world, this enormous *parque natural* (168,661 ha) occupies the *sierras*, just to the north of the Straits of Gibraltar. Humid, steep-sided gullies secreted within its depths harbour a unique assemblage of ferns, two of which – *Pteris incompleta* and *Psilotum nudum* – have their only continental European localities here. Europe's southernmost population of Roe Deer (*Capreolus capreolus*), 20 species of bat, the highest density of Egyptian Mongooses (*Herpestes ichneumon*) in Spain and 14 breeding raptors – including 20 pairs of Bonelli's Eagles (*Hieraaetus fasciatus*) – are the highlights.

36. Lagunas de Espera Three endorheic lagoons to the northeast of Cádiz, set among dry grasslands, Mediterranean scrub and cereal fields teeming with arable weeds, make up this diminutive *reserva natural* (47 ha). A large number of wintering and passage birds make use of these wetlands, with breeding water birds including such noteworthy species as the White-headed Duck (*Oxyura leucocephala*), Red-knobbed Coot (*Fulica cristata*) and Purple Swamp-hen.

37. Sierra de Grazalema This compact but spectacular limestone massif in western Andalucía harbours about 1,400 taxa of vascular plant, including many regional and Afro-Iberian endemics. The botanical highlight of this *parque natural* (53,439 ha) – also a Biosphere Reserve – is the relict Spanish Fir (*Abies pinsapo*) forest that clings to the precipitous northern slopes of the range. One of the largest concentrations of Griffon Vultures in Spain breeds in the deep ravines that dissect the massif, and most of the typical Mediterranean forest mammals are present in the surrounding forests and *dehesas*.

38. Fuente de Piedra The principal claim to fame of this enormous endorheic lagoon near Antequera is the huge colony of Greater Flamingoes – sometimes exceeding 20,000 pairs – that nests on the ancient saltpans in the centre, although the muddy margins also attract large numbers of waders in winter and during passage periods. This 1,476-ha *reserva natural* and Ramsar Site is also home to a good-sized colony of Gull-billed Terns (*Gelochelidon nilotica*), while the dragonfly and damselfly community is exceptional.

BELOW The renowned Spanish Fir forest of the Grazalema Natural Park clings precariously to the north face of the Sierra del Pinar.

ABOVE The Desierto de Tabernas, at the foot of the Sierra Alhamilla, is a superb example of Spain's semi-desert habitats.

39. Sierra Nevada National Park This behemoth of a mountain range is some 80 km long and rises to 3,479 m at Mulhacén – the roof of mainland Spain. Just a stone's throw from the Mediterranean coast in eastern Andalucía, it is Spain's largest national park (86,208 ha), lying at the heart of a vast *parque natural* and Biosphere Reserve of over 170,000 ha. More than 2,000 species of vascular plant occur here, of which almost 80 taxa grow nowhere else in the world. Many endemic invertebrates live in the highest reaches, as do more than 15,000 Spanish Ibex (subspecies *Capra pyrenaica hispanica*) and Europe's most southerly populations of the Snow Vole (*Chionomys nivalis*) and Alpine Accentor (*Prunella collaris*).

40. Desierto de Tabernas One of the most arid habitats in Spain, this pale, dusty landscape of gullied badlands would not look out of place on the moon. The xerophytic vegetation of this *paraje natural* (11,475 ha) in Almería is rich in endemic species, while the cliff-lined *ramblas* (dry watercourses) host an exceptional assemblage of breeding passerines, including Black Wheatears (*Oenanthe leucura*), Blue Rock Thrushes (*Monticola solitarius*) and Trumpeter Finches (*Bucanetes githagineus*).

41. Caldera de Taburiente National Park Covering the central and highest point of the Canary Island of La Palma – the whole

of which is a Biosphere Reserve – this 4,690-ha national park's focus is an enormous, sheer-sided volcanic crater some 8 km in diameter. Canary Pines (*Pinus canariensis*) clothe the slopes, with the deepest, most humid gorges housing fragments of *laurisilva* and the crests harbouring a diverse community of fissure plants, notable among which is the endemic *Viola palmensis*. Introduced Barbary Sheep (*Ammotragus lervia*) are the most visible mammals, with Red-billed Choughs (*Pyrrhocorax pyrrhocorax barbarus*) and Plain Swifts (*Apus unicolor*) among the most characteristic birds.

42. Garajonay National Park La Gomera harbours more than half of the Canary archipelago's laurel forests, with the finest examples lying within this 3,986-ha national park at the high point of the island. Ferns such as *Woodwardia radicans* and *Athyrium umbrosum* thrive in the half-light, while the tops of the trees are populated by Bolle's and Laurel Pigeons (*Columba bollii* and *C. junoniae*), both increasingly scarce species known only from the Canaries.

43. Frontera Covering 12,480 ha, this *parque rural* encompasses a magnificent thermophilic forest of Canary Junipers (*Juniperus canariensis*) and *Maytenus canariensis* on the northern edge of the island of El Hierro, the whole of which is a Biosphere Reserve. Nearby coastal crags are home to breeding Ospreys (*Pandion haliaetus*).

44. Cañadas del Teide National Park This is the oldest and most extensive of the Canary Islands' national parks, declared in 1954 and covering 18,990 ha at the summit of the island of Tenerife. Volcanic cones and lava flows are very much in evidence, harbouring a wealth of endemic plants and invertebrates, with summer bringing the spectacular *Echium wildpretii* into flower. The vertebrate fauna is poor, with Barbary Partridges (*Alectoris barbara*) and Kestrels (*Falco tinnunculus canariensis*) being the most abundant birds.

45. Corona Forestal One of the finest examples of mature Canary Pine forest in the archipelago, this *parque natural* covers 37,173 ha and completely encircles the Cañadas del Teide National Park. Among its more notable denizens are such

emblematic birds as the Blue Chaffinch (*Fringilla teydea tey-dea*) and Island Canary (*Serinus Canaria*).

ABOVE Canary Pines in the Barranco de las Angustias, Caldera de Taburiente National Park.

46. Dunas de Maspalomas A *reserva natural especial* covering 400 ha, this enormous active sand-dune system near the southern tip of Gran Canaria is sparsely populated with plants that are able to cope with the constantly shifting sands, such as *Traganum moquinii* and *Cyperus capitatus*. The most abundant vertebrate is the Gran Canaria Giant Lizard (*Gallotia stehlini*).

47. Corralejo The extensive sandy and stony plains near the north-east tip of Fuerteventura – a *parque natural* of 2,660 ha – are home to a fabulous assemblage of arid-land birds, notably the Houbara Bustard (*Chlamydotis undulata fuerteven-turae*), Cream-coloured Courser (*Cursorius cursor*), Eurasian Thick-knee (*Burhinus oedicnemus insularum*), Black-bellied Sandgrouse (*Pterocles orientalis*) and Trumpeter Finch (subspecies *amantum*).

48. Jandía At the other end of Fuerteventura, the badlands of the Jandía Peninsula harbour a rich endemic flora, with the spiny, cactus-like spurge *Euphorbia handiensis* perhaps taking pride of place. The *parque natural* covers 14,310 ha and is populated by similar birds to Corralejo, with the addition of the scarce Canary Islands Stonechat (*Saxicola dacotiae dacotiae*) and endangered Egyptian Vulture (*Neophron percnopterus majorensis*).

49. Timanfaya National Park The whole island of Lanzarote, including the offshore islets to the north, is a Biosphere Reserve, but the most dramatic scenery is undoubtedly that of the volcanic cones, craters and lava flows of the Timanfaya National Park (5,107 ha). Although at first sight this fairly recent volcanic landscape is devoid of life, the ochre and black rocks in fact support a diverse community of lichens and invertebrates, with the Atlantic Lizard (*Gallotia atlantica*) being perhaps the most abundant terrestrial vertebrate. Cory's Shearwaters (*Calonectris diomedea borealis*) breed on the north-facing coastal cliffs.

50. Archipiélago Chinojo The Riscos de Famara, along the north-western tip of Lanzarote, and the islands of the Chinojo archipelago plus their surrounding seas, together comprise a *parque natural* of 9,110 ha, within which the islets of Montaña Clara, Roque del Infierno and Roque del Este are a restricted-access *reserva natural integral*. Many endemic plants occur on the precipitous sea cliffs of Famara, while the remote islets harbour the most diverse seabird colonies in the Canaries, if not the whole of Spain, with six species of shearwater, petrel and storm-petrel breeding here, as well as Ospreys and Eleonora's Falcons (*Falco eleonorae*).

Glossary

alluvial Alluvial sediments are those deposited by slow-flowing rivers, often forming a floodplain on either side of a water-course or filling shallow basins in estuarine conditions. The term can also be applied to plant communities growing in such habitats, such as forests or grasslands.

alisios Spanish name given to the North East Trade Winds that affect the north-facing slopes of the western Canary Islands, creating a belt of cloud at 500–1,200 m for much of the year.

anaerobic conditions Those in which oxygen is absent.

autochthonous Referring to species that are indigenous (native) to a certain area.

barranco Spanish term for a steep-sided ravine, much used in toponymy in the Canary Islands.

bat detector Device used to detect the presence of bats by converting their echolocation ultrasound signals to audible frequencies. Different species of bat echolocate at different frequencies.

biomass Total weight of living and dead organic matter in an ecosystem.

bivoltine species Usually applied to insects – especially butterflies and moths – that have two broods and therefore two flight periods per year.

brackish Term referring to water that is saline, but less so than the sea, as occurs in estuaries with a strong input of fresh water from rivers, streams or rainfall.

bryozoans Small marine colonial invertebrates, sometimes known as moss-animals, belonging to the phylum Bryozoa, each of which possesses a box-like calcite skeleton and feathery tentacles with which it traps food.

calcareous Soils or bedrock that contain large quantities of calcium carbonate and can be regarded as basic or alkaline in character.

Carboniferous limestone Calcareous rock mainly originating from marine sediments laid down in the Carboniferous period (345–280 million years ago).

cavernicolous Inhabiting caves.

cetacean Member of the order Cetacea (whales and dolphins). Large aquatic, predominantly marine, air-breathing mammals, in which the forelimbs are modified to form paddles, the hind limbs are absent and the tail-fluke is horizontal and used for propulsion.

chasmophyte Plant that grows in rock crevices.

chenopod Member of the goosefoot family (Chenopodiaceae) of higher plants, including succulent, salt-tolerant species such as glassworts, sea-blites and saltworts.

chlorophyll Magnesium-containing green pigments that give plants their colour and absorb radiant energy from the sun for use in **photosynthesis**.

cirque Steep-sided hollow in a high mountain area fashioned by glacial activity. Cirques are generally circular in plan but open to one side (rather like an amphitheatre), and often contain small lakes.

continental climate One that is characterized by its remoteness from **oceanic** weather systems, generally displaying extremes of temperature in winter and summer, and also typified by low precipitation in many cases, as in the heartland of the Iberian Peninsula.

climax community, climax vegetation Final stage of a plant succession in which the vegetation has reached a state of equilibrium with the environment, at which point it is more or less self-perpetuating. Over much of Spain, the climax vegetation is forest, although under certain conditions, such as low temperatures (at altitude, for example), high aridity or fire, the communities never reach this stage.

composite Member of the daisy family (Compositae) of higher plants, characterized by having tiny flowers that are densely grouped together in heads that themselves resemble flowers.

convergent evolution Development of similar external morphology in unrelated organisms as a result of adaptation to the same environmental conditions.

cryophilic flora That which prefers to grow at very low temperatures.

decapod Member of the predominantly marine order of crustaceans known as the Decapoda (from the Greek *deka*, 'ten', and *podos*, 'foot'), which have five pairs of walking legs, for example crabs.

dehesa Spanish term for the savannah-like wood pasture created by clearing the original evergreen forests and leaving certain trees – usually evergreen or **marcescent** oaks – standing. *Dehesas* occur principally in south-west Iberia and were originally intended to provide winter grazing for livestock. The trees are pruned to produce umbrella-shaped canopies, both to cast maximum shade so as to avoid soil desiccation, and to optimize acorn production to provide food for the free-range Iberian black pigs that forage here in the autumn. Charcoal and cork are typical forestry by-products.

doline Steep-sided, enclosed depression in a limestone region, also variously known as a swallow-hole or sink-hole, created by the process of **karstification**.

detritivore Animal that feeds on dead organic matter, for example leaf litter.

echolocation Detection of an object by means of reflected sound, used principally in order to locate prey and for the purposes of orientation by bats, shrews and some cetaceans.

embryo dune First stage in the sand-dune vegetation succession, occurring immediately behind the strand-line and formed by sands blown inshore or thrown up by the sea, usually sparsely populated by plants with long root stocks, which are tolerant of shifting sands. Once stabilized, other species are able to colonize, giving way successively to primary, secondary and tertiary dunes.

endemic species One that is restricted naturally to a particular geographic region because of factors such as evolutionary isolation or response to physical conditions (soil type, climate, and so on).

endorheic lagoons Shallow water bodies that can only become established in flat-bottomed basins lined with impermeable soils, where water from small, rainwater-fed streams rising in the surrounding hills accumulates in the absence of an outlet to the sea. Because they usually occur in southern regions with very low summer precipitation and high levels of evaporation, many endorheic lagoons are seasonal. Substrata that are rich in mineral salts often confer a marked salinity on the water.

ericaceous species Plants belonging to the heather family (Ericaceae), often woody **perennials**.

European Habitats Directive Legislation produced by the EEC in 1992 that identifies species and habitats at risk and obliges member states to propose a series of sites for inclusion in a Europe-wide network of special areas of conservation, to preserve the biodiversity of the continent, known as Natura 2000.

Euro-Siberian Literally of, or pertaining to, both Europe and Siberia, but in a narrower sense specifying animals, plants or habitats of northern climes rather than the Mediterranean region.

gallery forest That which extends, ribbon-like, along the banks of a watercourse, also known as riverine or fluvial forest.

garrigue Low-growing secondary vegetation community usually less than 1m high, which is widespread in the Mediterranean basin. It is derived from the original forest and dominated by aromatic and/or prickly dwarf shrubs that are often **xerophytic** in nature.

gastropods Molluscs such as slugs and snails that possess a true head, an unsegmented body and a broad, flat foot.

geophyte Terrestrial plant that survives unfavourable conditions by means of underground storage organs such as tubers and bulbs.

gneiss Coarse-grained, banded metamorphic rock.

gypsophilous Referring to plants that thrive best on gypsum-rich soils or bedrock.

halophyte, halophytic vegetation Plants adapted morphologically and/or physiologically to grow in saline habitats, especially **chenopods**.

hibernation Strategy adopted by some vertebrates as a means of enduring the winter. The creature's metabolic rate is reduced to a minimum and it enters a deep sleep, surviving on food reserves stored in the body during the autumn.

holt Lair or den of an otter.

hydrophyte Plant that displays morphological and/or physiological adaptations that enable it to grow in water or very wet soils.

hydrozoan Member of a class (Hydrozoa) of multicellular, mainly marine and colonial creatures in the phylum Coelenterata (sea anemones, jellyfish and corals); both hydroid and medusoid forms are present.

insolation The amount of incoming solar radiation that is received per unit area of the Earth's surface, which tends to increase with altitude and with proximity to the equator.

karstification Chemical weathering process involving a reaction between dilute carbonic acid (the solution in water of free atmospheric and soil carbon dioxide) and **calcareous** rocks, typically **limestone**. The resultant karst landforms include **dolines**, uvalas and limestone pavement.

labiate Member of the mint family (Labiatae).

liane Any woody climbing plant rooted in the substratum that twines its way up through the trees in search of light. Sometimes known as a liana.

limestone Sedimentary rock laid down in warm, clear waters, composed principally of calcium carbonate.

lycaenids Small butterflies of the family Lycaenidae, including blues, coppers and hairstreaks.

Macaronesia Biogeographic region that encompasses five Atlantic archipelagos lying off the west coast of Africa. Madeira, the Açores (Azores) and the Selvagens belong to Portugal, from which the República de Cabo Verde achieved full independence in 1975, while the Canary Islands were annexed by Spain in the 15th century. The term is derived from the Greek *makaro*, 'blessed' or 'happy', and *nesos*, 'island'.

maquis Drought-resistant Mediterranean secondary scrub that is 1–3 m high – taller than *garrigue* – and is composed principally of evergreen shrubs with thick, leathery leaves. It generally develops where the original Mediterranean forest has been felled, burned or grazed.

marcescent Term used to describe certain trees whose leaves die in the autumn but do not fall from the tree until the new foliage develops the following spring.

melanic Animals whose skin hereditarily contains an excess of the dark pigment melanin, and are thus almost black.

Meseta Vast inland plateau – composed predominantly of limestone – that comprises the interior of Spain, with an average height of around 600 m. The plateau is sometimes divided into the north *Meseta* and the south *Meseta*, separated by the Sistema Central.

metamorphic rocks Pre-existing rocks that have undergone changes within the Earth's crust as a result of the application of pressure or temperature, or of the action of chemically active fluids.

microclimate Very local climatic conditions.

monocotyledonous plants Those pertaining to the Mono-cotyledonae. This is one of the two great divisions of the angiosperms (flowering plants) in which the embryo characteristically has but a single cotyledon (seed leaf) and the leaves are parallel-veined. Examples are orchids, lilies and grasses. By contrast, members of the Dicotyledonae usually have net-veined leaves and embryos with two cotyledons.

monospecific Genus that contains only one species.

mustelid Member of the family Mustelidae, small mammals in the order Carnivora represented by eight native species in Spain.

nidicolous Term referring to a young bird that hatches naked and helpless, and stays in the nest until it can fly.

nidifugous Term referring to a young bird that hatches covered with down and capable of locomotion, and is thus able to leave the nest soon after hatching.

oceanic climate One characterized by maritime influences.

odonates Dragonflies and damselflies belonging to the Odonata, a primitive order of predatory insects with two pairs of large, transparent wings and prominent eyes; the nymphs are aquatic.

oligotrophic Term used to describe waters poor in nutrients, usually with a low density of aquatic micro-organisms and scarce vegetation, although the level of dissolved oxygen is usually high, thus favouring fish species.

orogeny Mountain building, especially where an area of the Earth's crust is compressed over many millions of years by lateral forces to create mountain chains, or orogenic belts.

osmosis Process by which water or some other pure solvent passes through a semi-permeable membrane into a region of greater solute concentration so as to equalize the concentration of the two liquids.

ovoviviparous Term referring to species – particularly certain snakes and lizards – that give birth to young developed from eggs retained within the mother's body, but separated from it by the egg membranes. Nourishment for the developing embryos is provided by the disproportionately large yolks.

parenchyma Soft, spongy plant tissue composed of thin-walled cells, frequently permeated by air spaces.

passerine Bird belonging to the order Passeriformes, characterized by four-toed feet adapted for perching; mainly small birds such as thrushes, warblers, finches and sparrows, but also including crows. All other avian orders can be referred to as non-passerines.

pelagic In marine ecology, referring to organisms that inhabit the surface layers of the oceans beyond the continental shelf, and can be used to describe species as diverse as plankton and sharks. In ornithological terms, applied to seabirds that come to land only to breed, spending the rest of their lives far out to sea.

perianth segments Components of the two outer whorls of a flower, namely the calyx (made up of greenish sepals) and the corolla (composed of brightly coloured petals). In **mono-cotyledonous plants** such as lilies, the perianth segments – three sepals and three petals – are often almost identical and are referred to as tepals.

perennial Plant that normally lives for more than two seasons. Once it reaches maturity it produces flowers annually.

pH Value on a scale of 1–14 that provides a measure of the acidity or alkalinity of a medium. Neutral media have a pH of 7, with values less than 7 indicating acid media and more than 7 alkaline; the lower or higher the figure, the more acid or alkaline is the medium.

photosynthesis Series of metabolic reactions that occurs in green plants and certain bacteria whereby carbon dioxide is converted into organic matter using energy absorbed from sunlight by the **chlorophyll**.

plutonic Referring to a body of usually coarse-grained igneous rock formed at depth within the Earth's crust.

poikilothermic Referring to an animal that regulates its body temperature by behavioural means, such as basking in the sun or hiding under stones. Although such creatures – notably reptiles, amphibians and fish – are often called 'cold-blooded', when active their body temperature is little different from that of homoeothermic ('warm-blooded') birds and mammals.

pollinia (sing. **pollinium**) Coherent masses of pollen grains, each the product of a single anther and transported as a unit by pollinating insects; they are particularly characteristic of orchids (Orchidaceae) and members of the milkweed family (Asclepiadaceae).

polychaete Member of the essentially marine class Polychaeta (bristleworms). These distinctly segmented annelid worms possess paired, bristly projections on each body segment, which are used for locomotion in free-swimming forms, or for feeding in sessile species.

psammophilic plant One that typically grows in sandy habitats such as coastal dune systems.

pyroclastic Literally 'fire-broken', referring to the shattered fragments of volcanic rock that are often produced during explosive eruptions.

racemose inflorescence One in which the main axis continues to grow, producing flowers laterally; the youngest blooms are located at the tip.

relict Term applied to animals and plants that have survived a widespread change in conditions by retreating to small areas known as refugia, as for example the Arctic–Alpine plants of the Sierra Nevada, which were isolated on the highest peaks following the northwards retreat of the Quaternary ice sheets.

saprophyte Plant or fungus that derives its nutrients from decaying plant or animal matter, dung and so on. Saprophytic higher plants have frequently dispensed with the need for chlorophyll.

sclerophyllous Referring to plants – usually trees or shrubs – possessing small, hard leaves with a thick, leathery cuticle that reduces water loss, thus allowing them to survive during the prolonged summer drought so characteristic of Mediterranean climates.

sierra Spanish term for a linear mountain range.

siliceous Referring to rocks or soils rich in silica, often in the form of quartz.

stolon Lateral stem that grows horizontally, often rooting at intervals to form new plant.

stomata (sing. **stoma**) Small openings in the stems and leaves of vascular plants, allowing access for carbon dioxide and egress for oxygen and water. Each stoma is surrounded by guard cells that control the pore size.

symbiotic relationship That occurring between two dissimilar organisms living together in close association. These days the term tends to be used only to describe mutually beneficial species interactions.

tectonic Relating to deformation within the Earth's crust and its consequent structural effects.

Tertiary period Between 65 and 5 million years ago, when a large area of southern Europe was covered with semi-tropical forest.

thermophilic Referring to an animal or plant that thrives best in warm conditions.

transhumance Movement of livestock from one region of land to another, either horizontally or vertically, to take advantage of grazing available at different times of year. Examples are the sheep that travel from their winter pastures in Extremadura to the mountains of northern Spain at the beginning of summer, traditionally along drovers' roads known as *cañadas*; and the cattle that ascend from their winter quarters in the valleys to the high pastures of the Picos de Europa in the summer.

transpiration Extraction of moisture from the soil by plant roots, its movement up the stem to the leaves and its eventual exit through the stomata.

tree-line Level marking the limit of tree growth in high-altitude or high-latitude regions.

tunicate One of a group of marine animals known as sea squirts (phylum Urochordata) nowadays considered to be primitive chordates (animals with backbones). Although the sessile adult stage has a tough, leathery, pouch-like body, the larvae resemble tadpoles, possessing rod-like notochords in their tails.

Tyrrhenian Referring to animals and plants with a world distribution limited to the islands of Corsica, Sardinia and Sicily, extending westwards to include the Balearic archipelago.

ultrabasic Referring to igneous rocks that consist almost completely of ferromagnesian minerals to the virtual exclusion of quartz and feldspar. The most common ultrabasic rocks are **plutonic**.

umbellifer Member of the carrot family (Umbelliferae or Apiaceae), whose flowers generally resemble umbrellas.

UNESCO United Nations Educational, Scientific and Cultural Organization.

vascular plants Those that possess vascular tissues (xylem and phloem) through which water and nutrients are transported, including flowerless, spore-producing ferns, horsetails and their allies (Pteridophyta), and seed-bearing plants (Spermatophyta). They are sometimes referred to as higher plants.

viviparous Creatures that give birth to live young rather than laying eggs, especially placental mammals and marsupials, but also some reptiles and fish.

xerophytic vegetation Composed of plants that can grow in very dry conditions and display morphological adaptations – reduced and/or waxy leaves, the ability to store water and so on – to enable them to withstand periods of drought.

zygomorphic flowers Those flowers that are characterized by bilateral symmetry; that is, divisible in half in only one plane, usually vertically.

Further Reading

Alamany, O. and Vicens, E., *Parques Nacionales de España*, Lynx Edicions, 2003 (Barcelona).

Bañares, A. *et al.* (eds), *Atlas y Libro Rojo de la Flora Vascular Amenazada de España*, Dirección General de Conservación de la Naturaleza, 2003 (Madrid).

Barbadillo, L.J. *et al.*, *Anfibios y Reptiles de la Península Iberica, Baleares y Canarias: Guía ilustrada para identificar y conocer todas las especies*, Editorial Planeta, 1998 (Barcelona).

Beniston, N.T. and Beniston, W.S., *Wild Orchids of Mallorca*, Editorial Moll, 2000 (Palma de Mallorca).

Blanco, J.C., *Mamíferos de España I: Insectívoros, Quirópteros, Primates y Carnívoros de la Península Ibérica, Baleares y Canarias*, Editorial Planeta, 1998 (Barcelona).

Blanco, J.C., *Mamíferos de España II: Cetáceos, Artiodáctilos, Roedores y Lagomorfos de la Península Ibérica, Baleares y Canarias*, Editorial Planeta, 1998 (Barcelona).

Bonner, A., *Plants of the Balearic Islands*, Editorial Moll, 2004 (Palma de Mallorca).

Bota, G. *et al.* (eds), *Ecology and Conservation of Steppe-land Birds*, Lynx Edicions, 2005 (Barcelona).

Bramwell, D. and Bramwell, Z., *Wild Flowers of the Canary Islands*, Editorial Rueda, 2001 (Madrid).

Bramwell, D. and López, J.M., *Natural History of the Canary Islands: La Gomera (Pocket Guide)*, Editorial Rueda, 1999.

Castroviejo, S. *et al* (eds), *Flora Iberica: plantas vasculares de la Península Ibérica e Islas Baleares*, Real Jardín Botánico, 1986– (Madrid).

Clarke, T., *Birds of the Atlantic Islands: Canary Islands, Madeira, Azores, Cape Verde*, Christopher Helm, 2006 (London).

Clarke, T. and Collins, D., *A Birdwatchers' Guide to the Canary Islands*, Prion, 1996 (Huntingdon).

Crozier, J., *A Birdwatching Guide to the Pyrenees*, Arlequin Press, 2001 (Shrewsbury).

de Juana, E., *Aves Raras de España: un catálogo de las especies de presentación ocasional*, Lynx Edicions, 2006 (Barcelona).

Farino, T. and Lockwood, M., *Travellers' Nature Guide: Spain*, Oxford University Press, 2003 (Oxford).

Ferrer, M., *The Spanish Imperial Eagle*, Lynx Edicions, 2001 (Barcelona).

García, E. and Paterson, A., *Where to Watch Birds in Southern and Western Spain: Andalucia, Extremadura and Gibraltar*, Christopher Helm (A&C Black), 2008 (London).

Grunfeld, F.V., *Wild Spain: a Traveller's Guide*, Sheldrake Press, 1999 (London).

Hearl, G., *A Birdwatching Guide to Mallorca*, Arlequin Press, 2002 (Shrewsbury).

Hearl, G., *A Birdwatching Guide to Menorca, Ibiza & Formentera*, Arlequin Press, 2001 (Shrewsbury).

Hilbers, D. *The Nature Guide to the Coto Doñana and surrounding coastal lowlands*, KNNV Publishing (Crossbill Guides), 2005 (Netherlands).

Hilbers, D., *The Nature Guide to Extremadura, Spain*, KNNV Publishing (Crossbill Guides), 2006 (Netherlands).

Hilbers, D. *The Nature Guide to the Andalusian Sierras: from Málaga to Gibraltar – Spain*, KNNV Publishing (Crossbill Guides), 2007 (Netherlands).

López Gallego, A. *Donde Ver Aves y Naturaleza en Extremadura*, Ediciones Albarragena, 2000 (Badajoz).

Madroño, A. *et al.* (eds), *Libro Rojo de las Aves de España*, Dirección General para la Biodiversidad/SEO-BirdLife, 2005 (Madrid).

Martí, R. and del Moral, J.C. (eds), *Atlas de las Aves Reproductoras de España*, Dirección General de Conservación de la Naturaleza/Sociedad Española de Ornitología, 2003 (Madrid).

Montero, J.A., *Where to Watch Birds in Spain: the 100 best sites*, Lynx Edicions, 2006 (Barcelona).

Muddeman, J., *A Birdwatching Guide to Extremadura*, Arlequin Press, 2000 (Shrewsbury).

Palmer, M., *A Birdwatching Guide to Southern Spain*, Arlequin Press, 2002 (Shrewsbury).

Palmer, M. and Fidel, L., *A Birdwatching Guide to Eastern Spain*, Arlequin Press, 2001 (Shrewsbury).

Palomo, L.J. *et al.*, *Atlas y Libro Rojo de los Mamíferos Terrestres de España*, Dirección General para la Biodiversidad/SECEM-SECEMU, 2007 (Madrid).

Paterson, A., *Las Aves Marinas de España y Portugal: Península Ibérica, Islas Baleares, Canarias, Azores y Madeira (Seabirds of Spain and Portugal)*, Lynx Edicions, 1997 (Barcelona).

Pérez de Albéniz, J., *El Lince Ibérico: Una Batalla por la Supervivencia*, Lynx Edicions, 2006 (Barcelona).

Pleguezuelos, J.M. *et al.* (eds), *Atlas y Libro Rojo de los Anfibios y Reptiles de España*, Dirección General de Conservación de la Naturaleza/Asociación Herpetológica Española, 2002 (Madrid).

Ramos, E., *The Birds of Menorca*, Editorial Moll, 2000 (Palma de Mallorca).

Rebane, M. and García, E., *Where to Watch Birds in Northern and Eastern Spain*, Christopher Helm (A&C Black), 2008 (London).

Rodríguez Piñero, J., *Mamíferos Carnívoros Ibéricos*, Lynx Edicions, 2002 (Barcelona).

Romo, A.M., *Flores Silvestres de Baleares*, Editorial Rueda, 1994 (Madrid).

Varela Simó, J.M., *Aves Amenazadas de España*, Lynx Edicions, 2007 (Barcelona).

Verdú, J.R. and Galante, E. (eds), *Libro Rojo de los Invertebrados de España*, Dirección General para la Biodiversidad, Ministerio de Medio Ambiente, 2006 (Madrid).

Useful Contacts

In this day and age, a vast amount of information about Spain and its wildlife is readily available on the Internet, and there is simply not room here to list more than a few of the more reliable and informative websites.

http://www.vertebradosibericos.org/
Online encyclopaedia containing a wealth of information about the natural history of Spain's vertebrate fauna, from fish to mammals, in Spanish.

http://www.fauna-iberica.mncn.csic.es/
Fauna Ibérica is a government-sponsored scientific research project on the zoological biodiversity of the Iberian Peninsula and the Balearic Islands. Taxonomic inventories of the Spanish fauna are available for many invertebrate and vertebrate groups.

http://www.secem.es/
The website of the *Sociedad Española para la Conservación y Estudio de los Mamíferos* (Spanish Society for the Study and Conservation of Mammals).

http://www.seo.org/
The website of the *Sociedad Española de Ornitología* (Spanish Ornithological Society), a scientific and conservation society affiliated to BirdLife, founded in 1954.

http://www.fatbirder.com/links_geo/europe/spain.html
Fatbirder is perhaps the best birdwatching website to deal with Spain in English, with detailed information about the species and reserves of all parts of Spain, arranged by region.

http://www.rarebirdspain.net/
Up-to-the-minute information on the birds of Spain, in particular the rarities, in English.

http://www.herpetologica.org/
The *Asociación Herpetológica Española* (Spanish Herpetological Society) is the national organization for the study of reptiles and amphibians in Spain.

http://www.asociacion-zerynthia.org/
Spain's only national butterfly and moth conservation society, formed in 2006.

http://www.butterfly-guide.co.uk/regions/spain/
Europe-wide website about butterflies, in English, with a section dedicated to Spain.

http://groups.msn.com/odonata/
Comprehensive website dedicated to the dragonflies and damselflies of mainland Spain, in Spanish.

http://www.orquideasibericas.info/
A website for orchid lovers, with information about all the species present in Iberia, in Spanish.

http://www.anthos.es/
Anthos is a huge database compiled by Ministry of the Environment and the Royal Botanical Garden in Madrid, containing tens of thousands of records about the vascular plants of Spain. Search by species, genus or region, including the Canary Islands.

http://www.wwf.es/
WWF/Adena is the Spanish section of the World Wide Fund for Nature, founded in 1968.

http://www.iberianature.com/
A wealth of information about the nature and geography of Spain, in English.

http://www.wild-spain.com/
Information on nature and outdoor travel in Spain, with articles, photo galleries and news briefs, in English.

http://spainforvisitors.com/
A comprehensive English-language website about Spain and Portugal, with a link-rich section on birdwatching, nature reserves and the outdoors.

http://www.iberianwildlife.com/
English website containing illustrated articles about the wildlife and nature reserves of Spain, especially Extremadura, Andalucía, the Pyrenees and the Picos de Europa.

Index

Picture Credits

Front and back covers by Carlos Sánchez.

Carlos Sánchez/nayadefilms.com 1, 2, 3, 4–5, 6 (left), 8–9, 10, 13, 15, 17, 18–19, 20–21, 23, 26, 28 (top), 29, 34 (top), 35 (bottom), 36, 37, 38, 46, 49, 52 (top), 53, 54, 55 (top), 57, 59, 60 (right), 62, 63 (top), 65, 66, 67 (top), 71, 72 (top), 73, 74, 76, 77, 80, 82, 83 (top), 84, 85, 87 (bottom), 88–9, 91, 93 (bottom, right), 96 (left), 104 (right), 105 (left), 106 (bottom, left), 108 (bottom), 109, 110, 111, 113, 114 (top), 115, 116, 117, 118, 119, 120, 121, 122, 123, 124, 125, 126, 127, 128, 129, 130, 131, 132, 133, 134, 135, 136, 137, 139, 140, 141, 142, 144, 145, 146, 147, 148–9, 150, 151, 152, 154–5, 156, 158, 159, 160, 161, 162, 164, 164.

Teresa Farino 6 (right), 7 (left), 16 (top, below), 22, 24, 25, 27 (top, below), 30 (top), 31, 32, 33, 34 (bottom) 35 (top, centre), 39, 41, 42, 43, 44, 45, 50, 51, 52 (bottom), 55 (bottom), 56 (top), 58, 60 (left), 61, 63 (bottom), 64, 68, 69, 70, 72 (bottom), 78, 79, 81, 83 (bottom), 86, 87 (top), 90, 93 (top, left and right; bottom, left), 94, 95, 96 (right), 97, 98, 99, 100, 101 (top, left), 102, 103, 104 (left), 105 (right), 106 (top, left and right; bottom, right), 107, 108 (top), 112, 114 (bottom), 163.

Enrique Ballesteros/nayadefilms.com 75.

Carlos Martin/nayadefilms.com 28 (bottom).

José Luis Rodríguez/nayadefilms.com Spine, 7 (right), 47, 143.

Roger Tidman/nayadefilms.com 67 (bottom).

Juan Carlos Vicente/nayadefilms.com 30 (bottom), 56 (bottom), 101 (top, right; bottom).

Acknowledgements

During the 20-odd years that I have lived in Spain, I have encountered many of the country's most enthusiastic and erudite naturalists, who have shared their knowledge and passion for Spain's animals and plants unreservedly; although too numerous to mention individually, to them a heartfelt vote of thanks. I would also like to express my gratitude to James Parry, without whose tenacity this book would never have been written, and to my editor, Krystyna Mayer, who has done her utmost to accommodate my idiosyncratic style.

This book is dedicated to my family, especially my parents, who have always encouraged me to pursue my interest in wildlife; my sisters, who have wholeheartedly tried to make this possible, despite a multitude of logistic problems; and my children Aneira and Gabriel, who continually surprise me with their observations on the natural world and its denizens. I am deeply grateful to you all.